A TIME TO REAP

a celebration of East Yorkshire's agricultural history

Stephen Harrison

First published in Great Britain in 2000 by the Driffield Agricultural Society

ISBN 0-9538258-0-9

Published by
The Driffield Agricultural Society
The Showground, Kelleythorpe, Driffield, East Riding of Yorkshire, YO25 9DN
Telephone/Facsimile: 01377-257494
Registered Charity No.1068658

Printed and bound in Great Britain by
Horsley and Dawson Ltd
72-73 Middle Street South, Driffield, East Riding of Yorkshire, YO25 7QF
Telephone: 01377-253171; Facsimile: 01377-241968
e-mail: dmprint@driffield72.freeserve.co.uk

1. Typical Yorkshire Wolds scene: The Great Wold Valley at Weaverthorpe

Contents

Acknowledgements

No research is ever undertaken in a vacuum. Without the enthusiasm, support and active collaboration of a large number of individuals and institutions this book would never have seen the light of day.

Firstly, thanks goes to the Driffield Agricultural Society and its education sub-committee for commissioning this publication. In particular, John Johnston, Derek Megginson, Trevor Malkin, Malcolm Pearson, and John Gledhill provided much support, advice, and guidance as the project progressed. Their counsel has been invariably helpful.

Secondly, an especial thanks goes to all those individuals and institutions who freely gave permission for their photographs to be reproduced in this book; many also provided essential background information regarding their images. In alphabetical order, the contributors are: C. Byass (105, 104); Castle Museum, York (103); R. Chilvers (59); A.C. Coleman (23, 24, 61, 64, 109, 112, 115, 142, 156); C. Dee (15); Driffield Agricultural Society (17); Driffield Times (16, 90, 130, 146, 152); Driffield Young Farmers' Club (138, 139); P. Duggleby (41); J. Dunning (30, 56, 137, 141); W.W. Gatenby (39, 40, 43, 51, 69, 77, 78, 88, 100, 118, 119, 120, 123, 129); S. Harrison (2, 3, 8, 10, 11, 98); T. Harrison (47, 63, 65, 107, 108, 110); the late P. Hepworth (42, 57, 71, 122, 124, 128, 131); J. Hoggard (14, 54, 55); Lord Hotham (158); M. Hopps (1, 19, 46); Hydro-Agri (UK) Ltd. (49, 50, 66, 74, 85, 86, 94, 97, 111); J. Johnston (113, 145); JSR Ltd., Southburn (4, 52, 53, 72, 76, 80, 81, 83, 91, 101, 102, 125, 126, 153, 154); C. Ketchell (147); G. Kirkwood (36); M. Kirkwood (121); M. Middlewood (37, 38, 62); J. Norris (48, 157); A. Pexton (44, 45, 70, 75, 87, 89, 96); the late B. Pinkney (132); M. Plewes (27, 28, 29, 35, 58, 60, 68, 93, 99, 104, 116, 133, 134, 135, 136, 143, 144, 148, 149); J. Porritt (18, 67, 155); F.W.O. Richardson (117); G. Rivis (95, 106); G. Robinson (73, 150, 151); J. Robinson (140); J. Scholes (79, 82, 84, 127); Sir Tatton Sykes (5, 6, 7, 9, 12, 13, 21, 92); the late W. Thurlow (22, 25, 26, 32, 33, 34); and M. Watts (31).

The cover photograph, taken by Michael Hopps, was specially commissioned for this book. Getting all the equipment to the same place, at the same time, and on the same day, was a remarkable logistical achievement. That it happened at all was due entirely to the efforts of: Geoff Anderson, Noel Bannister, David Brown, Arthur Croft, Tim Ewbank, John Gledhill, James Hopper, Chris Howe, Mark Jibson, John Johnston, Philip Lambert, Trevor Malkin, Derek Megginson, Mark and James Morton, and Malcolm Pearson. Visual images have a power to convey ideas and record feelings that is perhaps unrivalled. The making of this photograph, an event in itself, has produced a unique record in terms of both historical accuracy and aesthetic appeal.

Others provided both oral and written testimony, access to documents, and general background information: A.R. Andrews; Peter Atkinson; Janet Bowes, Yorkshire Museum of Farming; Peter Caley; Arthur Clappison; John Cundall; Chris Dee; the editor and staff at the Driffield Times; Ray Duke; Andrew Grace; Abigail Harrison; the staff at the local studies libraries in Beverley, Bridlington, Malton and Scarborough; D.W. Lister; John Poucher; Dick Robinson; Adrian Robson; Sir Tatton Sykes; Tony Topham; Aubrey and Chris Welford; and Tony Wilson.

The production of this book has received generous financial support from the following: E.B. Bradshaw and Sons Ltd., the J.S. and E.C. Rymer Charitable Trust, Paul Richardson (Richardson Ford), and John Johnston (Cruckley Animal Farm). To all these sponsors, an especial thank you.

Thanks also goes to my adult education students in Bridlington, Driffield, Leven and Stamford Bridge, with whom, over recent years, many of the themes in this book have been rehearsed. Their stimulating discussions and pertinent observations, local knowledge and reminiscences, have touched many parts of what follows.

Lastly, grateful thanks to my partner Gill Scott, who provided the conditions under which this book was written. Without her indulgence, support, interest and patient editorial skills this work would have been much the poorer. To her, this book is dedicated.

1. Introduction

Ever since early prehistory, farming has been East Yorkshire's major industry and, until recently, most of the county's other industries were either supplying goods to the agricultural community or were based on farm products. Until the mid-twentieth century, every facet of life was shaped by the requirements of the agricultural cycle. And yet there is no book available which celebrates the immense importance of farming in the making of East Yorkshire. It is hoped that the present publication will go some way towards filling that gap.

In 1999, the present writer was commissioned by the Driffield Agricultural Society to produce a book of text and photographs celebrating the county's agricultural past. This is the result. The book aims to chart, through a montage of text and photographs, the development of farming in the region from earliest times to the present day, focusing on the dynamic interplay between successive human populations, the landscape and agricultural practices. Whilst the primary focus will be on the Yorkshire Wolds, other parts of the county are not excluded from consideration.

The book is divided into two parts. The first provides a broad overview of the development of farming in the county. It is largely a work of synthesis, drawing on the research, both published and unpublished, of a large number of amateur and professional archaeologists and historians working in East Yorkshire. Although some discussion will be included with regard to prehistoric and early historic agricultural practices, the main emphasis will be on examining the dramatic and far-reaching changes of the last 250 years or so. The second part consists of a selection of 158 historic and modern farming photographs, documenting the enormous changes in local agriculture since the 1870s. These have been brought together especially for this project, and most are published for the first time. Each is captioned with a description of the operation(s) depicted in the image, and, wherever possible, with its location and date.

It is a truism, but every picture *does* tell a story. The photographs selected for inclusion in this book are no exception, and an essay could be written on each of them. Unfortunately, except in a very few instances, space does not permit an extended discussion of the scenes and activities depicted. It is hoped, however, that the essence of each image is sufficiently captured in its accompanying description.

A word about the title of this book. **A Time to Reap** was deliberately chosen for its multi-layered meanings. *To everything there is a season and a time for every purpose under heaven; a time to sow, a time to reap.* These words from **Book of Ecclesiastes** literally sum up the farmer's life, reminding us of the ordered pattern of agricultural tasks through the year. As well, there is the metaphorical notion of gathering in a rich historical harvest of memories and photographs, which may well stimulate readers to reap from their own personal store of memories. At the beginning of a new century and a new millennium, the time is also ripe to collect the record of a way of life, constantly changing, but always following the rhythm of the farming year.

Finally, a note on weights, measures and money. The weights and measures used in this book are the ones contemporaries used. The standard unit for grain was the bushel (roughly 36 litres) of 4 pecks or 8 gallons, and 8 bushels made a quarter (about 2.9 hectolitres). The weight of a bushel of grain can vary, but a bushel of wheat weight weighs about 56 pounds or roughly 25 kilograms, a bushel of barley 48 pounds, and a bushel of oats 38 pounds. The unit of measurement for area was the acre, equivalent to about 0.4 hectares; linear measurement was by the mile, equivalent to about 1.6 kilometres. When area, weight and volume are related in measures of yield, 20 bushels per acre is approximately equivalent to half a ton per acre, which is about 500 kilograms per acre, 1.2 tonnes per hectare, and 17.4 hectolitres per hectare. Prior to 1971, the English pound (£) consisted of 20 shillings (s), each shilling comprised 12 pence (d), and a penny comprised 4 farthings. All quoted horse-power figures are approximate and are intended for informal comparison only. Traction engine power is quoted in nominal horse-power, which was in contemporary usage; this is based on cylinder measurement and bears no relation to the actual horse-power produced by the machine.

2. Setting the scene

With an area of 1,170 square miles, East Yorkshire is the smallest of the three Ridings into which Yorkshire is divided. This chapter relates to the historic county, and disregards recent local government boundary changes, which have resulted in parts of the area being transferred to the North Riding.

East Yorkshire has a certain geographical unity. Its boundaries are natural and well-defined: the North Sea forms the eastern boundary, the Vale of Pickering the northern, the Vale of York the western, and the River Humber the southern. It is also an isolated region. Until relatively recent times, prior to the large-scale drainage and reclamation of the surrounding lowlands, the areas along its landward boundaries acted as barriers, effectively reducing contact with the outside world. To a large extent, the region's distinctiveness is a product of this isolation, which encouraged idiosyncratic developments in culture, language and customs.

The county's identity has been shaped by its location. In common with neighbouring Lincolnshire and East Anglia, it is characterised by comparatively young rocks, smoothed by glacial erosion and smothered by glacial and post-glacial deposition. The terrain is flat or gently rolling. Soils are very varied and in most areas relatively deep and fertile. It also ranks as one of the driest counties in England, with an average annual rainfall, on the Yorkshire Wolds, of 32 inches, but other parts of the region receive less than 25 inches.

East Yorkshire can be divided into four main natural regions, each with, more in the past than now, distinctive landscapes, agrarian economies and societies:

1.   the Yorkshire Wolds at the centre;
2.   the Vale of York to the west;
3.   the Vale of Pickering to the north; and
4.   Holderness to the east of the Wolds.

The chalk of the Wolds, continuing the line of the Lincolnshire Wolds, forms an island of higher ground in an otherwise flat, low-lying region, and is a distinct geological and geographical entity extending over 300,000 acres. It dips to the south-east and, buried deep beneath later sediments, underlies the whole of the eastern part of the county. As a surface outcrop, the chalk takes the shape of a crescent, beginning on the River Humber foreshore at Hessle and terminating abruptly in the sheer sea-cliffs of Flamborough Head. From Hessle it extends north-west for 30 miles and rises to a maximum height of 814 feet above sea-level in the vicinity of Wilton Beacon, just to the south of Garrowby Hill. It then runs eastwards for a further 30 miles until it reaches the North Sea at Flamborough.

The arc of chalk has steep west- and north-facing escarpments, which are particularly pronounced at the north-west angle, where the outcrop meets the limestone of the Howardian Hills. Most of the land on the Wolds is between 164 feet and 650 feet above sea-level, and consists of gently rolling countryside dissected by numerous steep-sided dry valleys. This is in contrast to adjacent areas: the Vales of York and Pickering, to the west and north respectively, and Holderness to the east, are all lower, wetter areas, which make the Wolds, from a distance, appear rather like an island.

The most notable topographical feature of the Yorkshire Wolds is the 25 mile-long, broadly east-west, Great Wold Valley, through which the Gypsey Race flows from its source near Wharram-le-Street to the sea at Bridlington.

The majority of soils on the Wolds are derived from the chalky, flint drift deposits. These vary from heavy calcareous clays to freely drained loamy soils, which are found overlying chalk-gravels. In general, the soil cover is between 4 inches and 6 inches in thickness. Boulder clay covers the chalk on the eastern side of the Wolds to varying depths, which, in dry summers, holds water and thus makes crops less vulnerable to the effects of drought. On the higher Wolds, where the soil cover is much less, water for crop growth is obtained partly through root penetration into the fissures of the fractured chalk and partly as a result of higher rainfall, which, in this area, can reach 30 inches per annum.

The extent to which the chalk plateau is dissected is a major factor in the evolution of landscape and settlement. With the exception of the isolated farmsteads which came into existence during the eighteenth and nineteenth centuries, settlement on the Wolds has been concentrated in fairly well-defined locations, and consists of nucleated villages and hamlets: lines of villages are found in close association with springs along the base of the north- and west-facing escarpments, in an arc along the line of the east-facing dip-slope, just above the point where the chalk merges with Holderness, along the floor of the Great Wold Valley, and on the Flamborough headland moranic ridge.

From the Middle Ages onwards, the Wolds economy was dominated by sheep-corn husbandry. Nucleated villages were surrounded by their arable open fields, beyond which, on the higher, more exposed ground, lay vast expanses of scrubby sheepwalk. In the seventeenth century, these open and unimproved sheepwalks tended to favour the establishment of rabbit warrens and, a little later, the development of large landed estates. A large number of great country houses and landscaped parks, and estate villages and farms, can still be seen on the Yorkshire Wolds, bearing eloquent testimony to the ethos of agricultural improvement pursued by a small group of large, influential and progressive landowners in the eighteenth and nineteenth centuries, chief amongst whom was the Sykes family of Sledmere.

Today, the Wolds is intensively cultivated. In northern and central parts, over 85% of the area is in productive agricultural use, with wheat, barley and sheep fattening predominating. Oil seed rape is also grown, as well as sugar beet and peas on the lower land. Turnips, once so common on the Wolds, are now a rarity. Extensive potato growing is a feature of the higher Wolds, where lower temperatures reduce the risk of aphid infestation. Steep valley sides on the northern and western Wolds are still used as sheep pasture. The once so prolific pedigree Leicester Longwool sheep, reputedly introduced into the region in the early nineteenth century by Sir Tatton Sykes I and Squire Osbaldeston of Hunmanby, have, since the Second World War, been replaced by cross-breed ewes using Suffolk, Texel and other tups to produce finished lamb. Woodland is a feature of the steeper Wolds slopes, where arable farming is difficult, and among arable fields occurs in the form of shelter belts around farmsteads and as game coverts. Recently, agricultural practices aimed at reducing cereal production have resulted in a number of tree-planting schemes across the area. Beech, sycamore and larch grow well on the Wolds, but the shallow chalky soils are not suitable for conifers, especially on steep slopes.

To the west of the Wolds lies a narrow band of limestone country, known as the Jurassic Hills, between 98 feet and 230 feet in height, separating the Vales of York and Pickering from each other. To the south is the low-lying Vale of York, a stark open landscape complemented by wide skies. The Vale consists of a flat expanse of glacial deposits, with post-glacial alluvium, sands, peats, and lacustrine clays in many areas, and until systematic drainage in the eighteenth and nineteenth centuries was prone to widespread flooding. Crossing the Vale of York from the foot of the Wolds to the Pennines, and rising above the surrounding flat lands to a height of around 98 feet, the York and Escrick moraines provide natural routeways and dry, elevated areas for settlement.

Warping is a feature of those areas of the Vale of York adjacent to the River Humber, both as a result of natural and artificial processes. Flooding by soil-carrying tides meant that fertile silt deposits would be left on the land once the water had receded. In the past, much artificial warping took place, particularly in the Goole and Howden areas. This involved the deliberate flooding of land at high water, letting the silt settle and then draining off the water. The process was repeated until warp had been deposited to depths of between 2 feet and 3 feet By this method, poor sandy soils and acidic peaty ones were transformed into highly productive agricultural land.

The Vale of Pickering, separating the Wolds from the North Yorkshire Moors, is a flat low-lying alluvial plain, extending from Scarborough and Filey in the east to Helmsley in the west. The alluvial deposits rest on Kimmeridge Clay and were laid down at the end of the last Ice Age, when meltwaters from the retreating glaciers were dammed behind a moraine at the eastern end of the Vale. This layer of alluvium varies in depth, and at the eastern end there are substantial peat deposits.

Settlement in the Vale of Pickering is largely confined to two zones: in the south, below the chalk escarpment, a line of villages occupies an elevated position on a band of wind-blown sands overlooking the lower areas; and, in the north, a similar line of villages is located at the base of the North Yorkshire Moors.

The historic townships in the Vale of Pickering were laid out to take maximum advantage of the range of available resources and different soil types. They are long and narrow, and, on the southern side, extend from the High Wolds, down the chalk escarpment and out into the lowlands of the Vale itself. This arrangement allowed for the pasturing of sheep on the wold tops, arable cultivation on the easily worked soils around the villages, and the exploitation of a wide range of resources associated with the alluvial lands, including wildfowl, fish, reeds, peat and lush pasturage for cattle.

Holderness lies to the east of the Wolds. It is a low-lying area, nowhere higher than 180 feet above sea-level, and in many places between 25 feet and 65 feet. Geologically, Holderness is the youngest part of the East Riding. It is not an homogeneous area, but consists of glacially-derived, heavy, water-retentive boulder clays, interspersed with pockets of sand and gravel; and, along the margins of the River Hull and the north bank of the River Humber, there are intrusive alluvial deposits. Formerly, Holderness was characterised by numerous lakes or meres , which collected in the hollows of its gently undulating surface, and areas of marshland. In the eighteenth and nineteenth centuries these were drained as part of the process of agricultural improvement, and, today, Hornsea Mere is the only survivor of this once watery environment. These extensive drainage works turned Holderness into one of the most fertile regions within the East Riding. Here, intensive arable husbandry was practised, gaining the area an impressive reputation as a corn-producing district. This reliance on corn meant that the economic prosperity of Holderness was vulnerable to any fall in the price of cereals in the marketplace, as, in fact, occurred in the 1870s and 1880s.

Until modern times, settlement in Holderness, although extensive, followed a dispersed pattern, with small nucleated villages and hamlets located on glacial features, such as moranic mounds, or on boulder clay nodules , away from the near-permanent flood and marsh conditions then prevailing in the lower-lying areas.

Traditionally, the agricultural emphasis in the lowlands, with their rich pastures, was on cattle rearing and fattening. Flax and rye were also grown, as well as a range of lesser crops. Since the reclamations, enclosures and improvements of the nineteenth century, they have become much more diverse. Today, more than three-quarters of the agricultural land of Holderness is under arable cultivation, with wheat and barley being of equal importance. Potatoes are also extensively grown in the area. Livestock farming, as in the past, is still important. Dairy herds, supplying the milk requirements of Hull, are prominent, as are herds of fattening bullocks; pigs and poultry are also frequent sights. Sheep are only a minor element in the present agricultural economy of Holderness. Horticulture is a feature of areas adjacent to Hull. In the Vale of York, potatoes and other cash root crops, wheat, malting barley, peas, cattle and pigs provide the basis for a much less homogeneous

farming system than in other parts of the East Riding. Farming in the Vale of Pickering is very similar to that on the Wolds.

3. The farmers of prehistory

East Yorkshire is an old, long-settled landscape. Its present-day appearance is the product of a long sequence of development, extending back into prehistory. By way of background, this and the next chapter set out to reconstruct, in as far as the evidence allows, the agricultural practices of the various communities that inhabited the area between prehistory and the eighteenth century. Working on a broad canvas they will do no more than chart the general trends and significant developments evident in the archaeological and historical record, in order to provide a necessarily brief backdrop against which the dramatic and far-reaching changes of the last three hundred years can be measured.

Evidence for the earliest farming communities in the region is obscure, fragmentary, and often open to varying interpretations. However, despite these limitations, it is possible to present a broad overview of prehistoric and Roman agriculture, particularly for the Wolds.

East Yorkshire has been continuously occupied by people since at least the eighth millennium BC. Around 12,000 BC, the arctic conditions associated with the last Ice Age gradually came to an end. Across the British Isles, warmer temperatures, associated with the development of organic-rich forest soils and the appearance of a closed woodland, resulted in a dramatically changed landscape. The actual composition of the woodland varied from place to place, although everywhere it included a high proportion of lime, elm, hazel, oak, and pine. The megafauna of the Ice Ages disappeared, and the woodland was rapidly colonised by a wide range of animals, such as, for example, red deer, roe deer, elk, wild cattle, and pigs.

These animals, in turn, and the hunting possibilities they afforded, attracted the first human groups into the region.

The earliest evidence for people in the East Riding comes from the period known as the Mesolithic ('Middle Stone Age'), and dates to around 7,600 bc. Mesolithic people were not farmers in the accepted sense, but were hunters, gatherers and fishers. They consisted of small, highly mobile bands - perhaps family groups - exploiting the natural resources, and living in temporary campsites, such as those recently discovered at Eastburn, near Driffield. These people moved around large geographical territories, usually containing many different ecological zones, from which they derived a subsistence living - hunting the migratory herds of animals, fishing in the rivers and off coastlines, and harvesting the fruits and berries of the forests. The essential point about these very early societies is that they were living in balance - harmony - with their natural surroundings, taking only what was necessary to fulfill immediate needs and requirements.

During the later Mesolithic, there is some evidence from the Wolds that small areas of woodland were being cleared, by fire, presumably in an effort to improve the quality of grazing, and, thus, encourage and concentrate game, making hunting easier. Events such as this mark the beginning of the deliberate manipulation of the natural environment by people.

The first major, and semi-permanent, clearances of the wildwood seem to have occurred in the earlier Neolithic ('New Stone Age'), at the beginning of the fourth millennium BC, and are marked in the pollen record by a sudden decline of elm. The precise significance of this elm decline is not clear, but it was accompanied by an increase in the pollen of cereals and arable weeds, and must, therefore, have been associated with the activities of the first farmers.

Who were these farmers? Where did they come from? How was agriculture as a way of life introduced?

The change from a hunter-gather-fisher existence is associated with the gradual adoption of agricultural economies, perhaps introduced, initially at least, by small-scale movements of people from either Ireland or northern mainland Europe, who brought with them a *knowledge* of farming practices, as well as domesticated cattle and sheep - in fact, all the domesticated animals of today, except for the horse - and seed corn (emmer wheat, einkorn, and barley). This was part of a much broader pattern of economic and cultural innovation which swept across the temperate forest lands of north-west Europe during the fifth and fourth millennia BC.

Over time, the indigenous Mesolithic societies were succeeded by communities practising agriculture and having advanced flint and stone-working technologies, pottery-making skills, and complex social and religious practices, which found expression through the construction of the first earth and stone monuments; this was a protracted process, involving the the transference of technology and resources which were, at first, integrated into existing patterns of life and then, later, became dominant. By the mid-fourth millennium BC, the new exploitative activities had affected the natural forest cover of the British Isles, creating permanent open landscapes in many areas, thus effectively initiating the natural environment to create the first man-made landscapes.

The chalklands of the Yorkshire Wolds, enjoying a wide and favourable range of natural resources, became, along with Wessex and Orkney, a major focus for human settlement during the Neolithic.

Within East Yorkshire, there is very little definite evidence for Neolithic settlements, beyond the finding of occasional pits, post-holes and occupation floors , such as those discovered during building work at Mill Street, Driffield, in 1989. Here, a number of post-holes, tentatively identified as the remains of a rectangular house, together with a quantity of flint artefacts, were recovered. Other pits, and associated cultural material, form clusters in areas adjacent to the Woldgate, in the vicinity of Rudston, Boynton and Carnaby, and have been interpreted as domestic in nature, although, here, an alternative, ritual function may be equally relevant.

Evidence for Neolithic agricultural practices in East Yorkshire is scattered and piecemeal. Examination, between 1965 and 1969, of the pre-barrow soils sealed beneath the Kilham long barrow suggested that the site had formed part of an arable cultivation zone on at least two separate occasions, separated by a period of woodland regeneration. This may represent some form of shifting arable farming practice, intensively cultivating small areas until soil fertility became exhausted and then moving on to new locations to begin the process all over again, creating an unstable and fluid mosaic of woodland and areas of more open or cleared ground.

Elsewhere, as in the Rudston and Caythorpe areas, a number of possible storage pits containing preserved cereal grains - emmer, bread wheat and barley - have been discovered. This, together with chance finds of flint sickles from locations across the East Riding, points to the widespread adoption of cereal farming during the Neolithic, but just how important this was in the overall economy is not, at present, known.

The frequent finding of the bones of domesticated cattle, sheep and pig indicate that pastoralism formed an important element in the local economy. The comparatively high numbers of pig and cattle bones, in contrast to those of sheep, from sites in the Rudston area, together with those of deer, strongly suggests that there was still much woodland on this part of the Wolds during the Neolithic.

The contents of excavated pits also reveal that wild food resources were still, as in the preceeding Mesolithic, fully exploited, and formed an important dietary component. Quantities of carbonised hazel nut shells were found in two pits at Leven, and, from similar structures near Rudston, apple, crab apple and pear remains have been discovered. Butchered deer bones, and seafish bones and shells from sites in close proximity to the coast, are indicative of hunting and a varied diet.

All in all, the Neolithic economy may be characterised as mixed, with farming and hunting and gathering being of equal importance in wresting a living from a barely tamed landscape 4,000 and more years ago.

Around 2,000 BC the Neolithic began to give way to a new cultural formation: the Bronze Age. Locally, the archaeological evidence for the earlier part of the Bronze Age, up to c.1,400 BC, is dominated by the burial record. Despite nearly two hundred years of archaeological research, we know virtually nothing of the domestic activities of people during this time. By analogy with evidence from elsewhere, it is assumed that local societies were living in small farmsteads scattered across the landscape and practising a mixed arable-livestock farming regime. The areas closest to the farmsteads would be given over to the cultivation of barley and wheat in small fields, while the landscape beyond would have been dominated by extensive pastures of short, scruffy and scrubby grasslands. Here, sheep and cattle would have grazed. Given the absence of fertilisers, the arable areas would have quickly become exhausted, and so it is possible to envisage a patchwork landscape with settlements and their surrounding fields frequently relocating to new positions.

For the later Bronze Age, the concern with landscapes of the dead gave way to a concern with landscapes for the living. This was a time when the earlier emphasis on ancestry and the dead, expressed through a landscape dominated by monumental ceremonial and ritual structures, gave way to an over-riding concern with natural fertility, a period during which the landscape was transformed around the needs of food production. For the period after c.1,400 BC the evidence for domestic activity is clearer, but still far from complete. Perhaps the most significant development of this time, particularly on the Wolds, was the construction of long distance boundaries in the landscape. Despite considerable study over the last one hundred or so years, these linear earthworks, known as "entrenchments" to the nineteenth century antiquarians, remain ill-understood. What little archaeological evidence there is suggests that they were first constructed during the later Bronze Age.

Known locally as dykes, these single and multiple ditch and bank earthworks appear to divide the Wolds into large discrete territories, and point to a large-scale reorganisation of the landscape during the later Bronze Age and a possible shift from a predominantly arable farming system to an economy based more on pastoralism. This shift may indicate, perhaps, a response to climatic deterioration and/or a decline in soil fertility. The magnitude of the undertaking presupposes either strong hierarchical and centralised social and political control, or great inter-communal co-operation between smaller, more autonomous communities. Whatever the case, a great deal of communal effort must have gone into the construction of the dykes.

Such land boundaries, constructed in what was, by then, a largely treeless environment, obviously had functional uses. It is clear from both their construction and disposition that they are not defensive in character. They may have been stock enclosures, designed to separate the herds and flocks of different communities, or they may have acted as demarcators for different areas of land-use. As well as functional uses, however, the earthworks would have had a broader significance to the communities that built and maintained them. They are central elements in the social and symbolic landscape, emphasising a sense of communal identity, as well as rights of access to, and use of, the land they enclosed. Through the act of construction and the placing of human-engendered physical structures on the landscape, the dykes re-emphasise chosen boundary lines and related patterns of land-use. The imposition of physical boundaries renders the organisation and tenure of land more static and less open to question or later change.

The sheer monumentality of the dyke system across the Wolds is difficult for us, at this remove, to visualise. Snaking across the countryside, great bands of white chalk rubble, perhaps topped by some form of hedging or fencing as additional stock-proofing measures, and white-sided chalk-cut ditches, highlighted against the verdant greens of the background vegetation, must have presented an impressive sight to onlookers some three thousand years ago. The overall visual and symbolic impact would have been further reinforced by the periodic maintainance required to keep the dykes in good working order.

Subsequently, in the succeeding Iron Age (from c.750 BC until the incorporation of East Yorkshire into the Roman Empire in AD 70-71), the later Bronze Age dykes provided a framework within which further enclosure took place. The areas which they bounded were progressively sub-divided into smaller field systems comprising single ditch and bank enclosures - to some extent, similar to the patchwork of fields that are so familiar to us today.

Evidence for this new phase of enclosure can be detected on aerial photographs over much of the region. The clearest picture of this process at work has, however, emerged from excavations, during the 1970s and early 1980s, in Garton Slack and Wetwang Slack, a gravel-floored valley system on the Wolds, to the west of Driffield. Here, progressive enclosure can be demonstrated as having occurred throughout the Iron Age: during the third and second centuries BC, a large tract of land along the valley, bounded to the north by a pre-existing dyke and to the south, along the valley floor, by a long-used trackway, was enclosed. The area was sub-divided into large enclosures, each containing about three-quarters of a square mile, by the construction of new north-south banks and ditches, extending from the trackway up to the aforementioned dyke; later, probably in the first century BC, these large units were further sub-divided into a number of smaller areas forming rectilinear field systems, with each individual field being around one-and-a-quarter acres in size.

It is thought that this progressive enclosure represents a fundamental shift in farming practices, from, in the earlier Iron Age, an economy based primarily on cereal production, to one, in the later part of the period, centred more on stock raising. These changes are also associated with an expanding population and the development of hamlet and village-type communities, and can be interpreted as an attempt to rationalise and use more effectively the limited resources available.

Although it is always dangerous to extrapolate from the particular to the general, evidence is now accumulating to suggest that the sequence of events uncovered in Garton Slack and Wetwang Slack can be replicated over much of the Wolds and adjoining areas. If this is the case, we need to visualise a late Iron Age landscape dominated by small fields and a nucleated settlement pattern. In other words, each village or hamlet was surrounded by its own fields, which were farmed by individual families; and communities were linked to each other and to the wider world by a network of inter-connecting tracks and lanes.

The pattern of small enclosed fields and nucleated settlements established in the Iron Age continued in use, and was added to, throughout the Roman period. During this time, the importance placed on animals as symbols of wealth appears to have diminished and the ever-increasing demands of a common Roman market, extending almost to the limits of the then known world, brought about a gradual return to large-scale cereal production in the East Riding, as it did elsewhere.

4. Medieval and early modern farmers

With the collapse of the Western Roman Empire and the consequent withdrawal of its military and bureaucratic presence from Britain in AD 410, the country became vulnerable, in the fifth and sixth centuries, to colonisation by the Anglo-Saxons, and then again, in the ninth century, by the Vikings. Throughout this time East Yorkshire formed part of the great kingdom of Northumbria.

Much still remains to be discovered about the Anglo-Saxon and Viking settlement of the East Riding, but it seems that the indigenous population was gradually assimilated into the cultures of these newcomers, whose settlements were located in areas formerly occupied during the Romano-British period. Topographically, the most desirable settlement areas seem to have been along the fringes of the Wolds, and in some isolated parts of Holderness where glacially-derived sand and gravel mounds would have provided high and dry places on which to construct dwellings and other buildings.

Within the above framework, it appears that, throughout this period, settlement was scattered across the landscape, either in the form of individual farmsteads or as small, loosely organised villages, such as that excavated at Heslerton, on the southern fringes of the Vale of Pickering, between 1978 and 1982. Recent evidence from Eastburn suggests that many of these settlements, particularly the farmsteads, were short-lived and migrated across the landscape; presumably due to fairly rapid soil exhaustion, necessitating moves to adjacent, more fertile areas.

The occupied areas incorporated zones of agricultural activity, including arable, pasture and, where available, meadow, with large tracts of waste land and pockets of woodland beyond. Those settlements near rivers, streams, meres and marshy areas would also have exploited a wide range of other natural resources associated with those particular environments, for example, fishing and wildfowling.

The period between the Norman Conquest of 1066 and the early years of the fourteenth century saw far-reaching changes in the rural economy of East Yorkshire (as, indeed, it did elsewhere). Unparalleled expansion was the dominant theme of those years. It was a time of major population growth (overall, during this time, the country's population expanded from an estimated 4 million in 1086 to an estimated 8 million by the turn of the thirteenth century), which necessitated a reorganisation of agriculture and settlements. Under favourable, and stable, climatic conditions, agricultural production was pushed to its limits, aided by innovations and improvements in the tools and techniques of husbandry. In particular, this meant that more marginal areas, such as the low-lying intractable claylands, could be brought into cultivation for the first time.

Nucleated settlement was the norm over much of the East Riding at this time. The villages were surrounded by two, three or more large, open, arable fields, which were divided into strips (ridge and furrow, the corrugated effect which can still be seen preserved in grassed fields). Villagers were each allocated a number of strips, which were distributed across the whole field system. Whilst the strips were farmed individually by the villager concerned, the management and regulation of the open fields *as a whole* was vested in the community of holders and administered through the manorial court. Beyond the arable zone lay areas of unenclosed common pasture, meadow and woodland.

The arable areas were normally operated on a two- or three-course rotation, with one-third of all land lying fallow at any one time. A wide range of crops was grown across the region: barley was grown on the less fertile soils as it made fewer demands on the land, naked or wheat barley was grown on intermediate soils, and long-eared or spratt barley predominated on the better land; both winter and summer varities of wheat were also grown, including Buckwheat or French wheat; maslin, or massledine, a mixture of wheat and rye, had a relatively wide distribution over the area, as did oats; and clean rye was favoured on the light, gravelly, dry soils of the many Wolds valley floors. Documentary sources also mention the cultivation of a range of other crops, including beans, flax, mustard, onions, peas, and saffron.

Another feature of the medieval rural landscape was the monastic grange, large farmsteads established by the various religious houses of the region, and which were normally sited away from existing centres of population. The granges can be classified into one of two types: (1) those which were devoted to livestock rearing - sheep on the Wolds and usually cattle in more low-lying districts, and (2) those which were primarily arable units.

The medieval agricultural year may be summarised in the following manner:

Late June/July: Haymaking.

Early August: Haymaking completed; meadows then broken , ie opened for animals to graze.

August: Beginning of harvest; winter corn field harvested.

Late August/early September: Winter corn field broken , ie stock allowed to graze the stubble. Farmers begin harvesting the spring corn field.

October: Spring corn field broken , ie stock allowed to graze the stubble.

October/November: Fallow field ploughed, harrowed and sown with winter corn.

Early November: Meadows closed.

Late November: All animals leave the open fields, except for a stated number of sheep allowed to remain on the fallow field.

November/December: Preparation of new spring corn field for planting in the following spring.

March: Spring corn field sown.

April: Stock turned out in to meadows.

Spring: Lambing, calving, and farrowing of sows.

A consequence of population growth was that more land was put under the plough at the expense of pasture. Livestock numbers declined, and because there was less manure to spread on the land soil fertility gradually became exhausted, inevitably reducing yields.

Towards the end of the thirteenth and the beginning of the fourteenth centuries this period of phenomenal growth began to falter and then to be reversed. The fourteenth century is seen as a severe and prolonged recession. There was a major downturn in climatic conditions, the weather becoming much colder and wetter, and this resulted in a whole series of harvest failures, a situation exacerbated by falling yields due to soil exhaustion. Harvest failures brought about widespread scarcity and famine, resulting in malnutrition and a lowering of the population's resistance to disease. Consequent upon this, a whole range of diseases became endemic, including diphtheria, dysentry, scurvy, smallpox, and typhus, resulting in high mortality rates. And then, between 1348 and 1351, bubonic plague - the Black Death - ravaged the population. In total, the country's population was halved, from eight to four million, during the course of the fourteenth century. Over the next four hundred years population levels remained constantly low, not recovering to the pre-fourteenth century high until the 1740s-50s.

All in all, it was a period of prolonged demographic recession associated with a corresponding scaling down of prevailing levels of economic activity. One of the principal consequences of this reversal was the shrinkage and, in many cases, the complete desertion of numerous villages.

During the later stages of the fifteenth century, but more particularly throughout the sixteenth, English agriculture underwent a further period of transformation. Over much of lowland England there was a change of land use from arable farming to the rearing of sheep. This was associated with a reduced demand for food, but more particularly with the expansion of the woollen clothmaking industry in the West Riding and further afield, and the ever increasing demand for the raw material that this generated. Quite simply, it became more profitable for landowners to rear large flocks of sheep than it was to continue with arable cultivation. Accordingly, large areas of arable were enclosed and converted to sheepwalk. This resulted in the depopulation, or desertion, of many villages. People were surplus to requirements under the new agrarian regime and were simply ejected from their villages, their homes demolished and the entire area laid down to grass. Where previously a village might have had a population of one or two hundred people, it was replaced by one or two shepherds and their families. As Thomas More wrote in 1517:

Sheep ... These placid creatures, which used to require so little food, have now apparently developed a raging appetite, and turned into man-eaters. Fields, houses, towns, everything goes down their throats.

There are many villages in the East Riding, but particularly on the Wolds, which suffered this fate: for instance, Cottam, Swaythorpe, and Wharram Percy.

Commercial rabbit warrens were a characteristic feature of seventeenth century East Yorkshire, again, particularly, on the Wolds. These warrens, frequently extending over several hundred acres, were usually sited in marginal areas, on, for example, the High Wolds or on pockets of less fertile sands in the Vale of York. During this period warrens were established at Arras (17th. century), Barmby Moor (1655), Harpham Moor (1666), Gardham (1687), Hayton (1610), Hunsley (1685), Linton (1602), and Risby

(1592). In the following century, they were joined by Argam (1758), Blanch (1749) Cottam (1732), Cowlam (1743), Craike Hill (1700), Drewton (1749), Driffield and Kelleythorpe (1719), Eastburn (1729), Enthorpe (1750), Flamborough (1758), Arden Fleets (1739), Hessleskew (1717), Hunmanby (1713), Kilnwick Wold (1718), South Cliffe (1760), Sunk Island (1711), and Weedley (1752). The warrens themselves were self-contained units, sometimes located on the sites of deserted villages, surrounded by a perimeter boundary wall of earth surmounted by a hedge, or a timber fence - even so, this did not prevent rabbits escaping and causing damage to surrounding crops, much to the indignation and annoyance of neighbouring farmers! - and containing a warrener's house and various outbuildings.

At their height, warrens occupied an estimated 15,000 to 18,000 acres within the East Riding. They were commercial enterprises, each warren containing several thousand breeding pairs of rabbits, yielding, in total, between 100,000 and 150,000 couple of rabbits annually. Following slaughter, the skinned carcasses were sold for meat in the industrial towns of the West Riding, and in York, Hull, Beverley and the other towns in the region. In the early nineteenth century, the rabbits were conveyed to these places in *covered carts, containing from six to eight hundred couples, strung on rods, and suspended across the cart one tier above another.* The skins were dried before being sold to furriers; although some of the rabbit fur was used locally, the bulk was sent to other parts of the country, in particular to London and Manchester.

Unique amongst the surviving East Riding agricultural records of the seventeenth century is the justly famous **Farming and Memorandum Books** of Henry Best (c.1592-1645) of Elmswell, near Driffield, most recently republished in 1984 under the editorship of Donald Woodward. This collection contains an immense amount of detail regarding the topography and the layout, organisation and working of the 1293-acre estate during the first half of the seventeenth century, offering a multitude of insights into the agricultural history of the period. Essentially, it consists of a series of individual treatises and rememberances, providing a unique account of farming practices, of the marketing of agricultural produce, and of rural customs in the years leading up to the English Civil War. Compiled in the early 1640s, it is a book of instruction, a manual, written by a *practising* farmer, and was almost certainly produced for the benefit of Henry Best's son and heir John (1620-1669). As one of only two surviving English farming books from the seventeenth century, it has long been recognised as of crucial importance in any understanding of English agricultural practice during that period.

By the beginning of the eighteenth century, the East Yorkshire landscape was still very much medieval in character, with 70% of all villages still surrounded by their open field arable systems, pasturelands and meadows, and small areas of woodland, and whose inhabitants still farmed in traditional ways. Although much had changed between the eleventh and seventeenth centuries, even more dramatic transformations were about to take place.

5. An enclosed landscape

Between the mid-eighteenth and mid-nineteenth centuries, the face of East Yorkshire was transformed by the large-scale enclosure of the remaining medieval open fields and common land. During this time, a pattern of settlement and land-use which had slowly evolved over many centuries was overlaid, but nowhere entirely obliterated, by a new landscape. This new landscape was more regular and more efficient, and, in all its essential components, survives intact to the present-day.

Enclosure by act of parliament was largely responsible for this transformation. Enclosure was the replacement of large open fields surrounding a village, whose strips were owned individually but whose cropping and stocking were controlled, according to ancient rights and customs, by the community of owners, with smaller, individually owned fields whose management could be controlled by the owner.

The following extract, from a poem written by Kilham-resident Edward Anderson sometime in the 1820s, gives an impression of the changes wrought by enclosure in and around the village. In somewhat idyllic language, he writes:

> But when the town of Kilham first I saw,
> The walls were mostly clay, and thatch'd with straw,
> What alterations in a little while!
> The houses now are mostly brick and tile;
> They've built a poor-house, and a large new mill,
> And cut away How, Butt, and Butcher-Hill;

> Besides improvements which the town does yield,
> We see new houses built about the field;
> A diff'rent view we see at the town end,
> Where boys they us'd the geese and pigs to tend;
> You saw the green spread o'er with geese and
>   feathers,
> And cattle then confin'd with stakes and tethers;
> The corn destroy'd, all round the town you saw,
> And for some distance, nothing left but straw.
> Since 'twas inclos'd but nine and thirty years,
> The ground is much improv'd it now appears;
> The springing corn which oft has blasted been,
> By frost winds, so cold, so sharp and keen,
> Now shelter'd is, no more the storm needs dread,
> But cheerful lifts its little drooping head;
> The cattle they no shelter then could find,
> Except in dales where sun scarce ever shin'd:
> Screen'd by the trees, now in the shade can lay,
> On hills find shelter on a stormy day;
> The sheep that oft were lost in drifts of snow,
> Shepherds to find them knew not where to go;
> When drifted now, can easily be found,
> The fences keep them on their owners ground,
> In harvest when it came a windy day,
> The sheaves and pea-reaps oft were blown away,
> Mixt, and against some balk or hill were blown,
> The farmers then they could not know their own;
> Some then would take advantage of the rest,
> At such a time the strongest man far'd best,
> This caus'd disputes which they could not prevent,
> Some suff'ring loss were forc'd to be content;

Neighbour 'gainst neighbour had perpetual jars,
Town against town were constantly at wars;
He who so rash as for his friend durst plead
Was like to get a blow or broken head ...

A rather more sober account, written by agriculturalist John Caird in the early 1850s, towards the end of the enclosure process, but echoing Anderson's sentiments, describes the general Wolds scene in the following manner:

The country is all enclosed, generally by thorn hedges; and plantations, everywhere grouped over its surface, add beauty to the outline, while they shelter the fields from the cutting blasts of winter and spring. Green pasture fields are occasionally intermixed with corn, or more frequently surround the spacious and comfortable homestead. Large and numerous corn ricks give an air of warmth and plenty, while the turnip fields, crowded with sheep, make up a cheerful and animated picture.

Whilst a small number of townships and parishes underwent complete or, more commonly, partial enclosure prior to the 1740s, the process gained momentum and became institutionalised from the second half of the eighteenth century. Parliamentary enclosure was not a localised phenomenon, but affected most of lowland England during these years. Countrywide, by the 1860s, some eight million acres had been enclosed, totally transforming the face of the English landscape.

The motives behind enclosure were complex. The old, open field, strip farming system of the middle ages was increasingly seen as outmoded and inefficient; there was a general desire to improve productivity. These two motives were given general expression in all enclosure acts:

... And whereas the lands and grounds belonging to the several proprietors in the open fields, Ings and marshes, lie intermixed and dispersed in small parcels, and the same and also the ... common pastures, and other common and wastelands and grounds in their present state are incapable of much improvement, and would be of great advantage to the proprietors if the [parish] ... were divided and enclosed, and specific parts allotted to the several persons interested therein, in proportion to their respective properties, rights of common and other interests ...

Further motives to enclose can be summarised. Improvements in productivity were linked to new demands being placed upon agriculture by a rapidly growing, predominantly urban-based, population. Between 1741 and 1801, the population of England and Wales rose from 6 to 8.9 million, and the following half-century saw the growth accelerating to 17.9 million, and, by 1911, population levels had reached 28.4 million. In 1801 only 20% of the population lived in towns with more than 5,000 inhabitants. By 1851, this proportion had reached 54%, and, by 1911, it was around 70%. There was also the need for the country to become self-sufficient in foodstuffs, especially during wartime, when Britain was susceptible to blockade, as happened during the Napoleonic Wars. Also, linked to enclosure, and providing a further motive, were contemporary improvements in husbandry: new cropping techniques (eg the alternate use of fodder and cereal crops to abolish fallow, keep soils in condition, and provide food for animals), new livestock breeds (eg Dishley longhorn cattle, and New Leicester sheep), new implements (eg the horse-drawn hoe, and threshing machines), and management techniques (eg drainage, and the treatment of soils with marl, chalk, and bone) all went hand-in-hand with enclosure. Only through enclosure were the full benefits of the new husbandry to be enjoyed.

There were three routes to enclosure: first, before 1800 each township which wanted to proceed with enclosure had to have an individual Act of Parliament passed, specific to that place; second, after 1800, and because of the large costs involved with the passing of individual acts, a General Enclosure Act was passed by parliament. This had the effect of cutting costs and speeding up the process; and, third, a small number of enclosures took place without recourse to parliament, by general agreement between the parties concerned. Whatever, enclosure was a costly business to the communities involved: it has been estimated that the cost ranged from 4s. or 5s. an acre to as much as £4 or £5, with a probable average of around £2.

Enclosure was also a complex, and often lengthy, procedure, which involved a number of clearly defined incremental stages:

1. Meetings of the main owners of land and common rights in the township to discuss the desirability of enclosure. The probable costs would be considered, and the likely financial gain which would follow enclosure would certainly be prominent factors in any decision reached.

2. If agreement was reached, notices of the decision to enclose would be placed on the parish church door and in local newspapers, and a petition was presented to parliament requesting an Act to enclose the parish or township.

3. The Enclosure Bill was introduced in the House of Commons, considered in Committee, and passed through the normal parliamentary procedure. It then became an Act.

4. The Act contained detailed provisions which had to be observed in carrying out the enclosure. The Act named the Enclosure Commissioners (the officials empowered to effect enclosure), specified their powers and listed their duties. An enclosure act may be thought of as a detailed book of rules for enclosing a township.

5. After the passing of the Act, the commissioners, surveyor, and their assistants, began work. A detailed survey and plan was made of the entire area to be enclosed.

6. All people who claimed to own land and/or common rights had to submit their claims, in writing, to the commissioners. The commissioners heard evidence in support of, or in opposition to, these claims, and on that basis they accepted, modified, or rejected claims.

7. All existing holdings and rights of common were viewed and valued by the commissioners.

8. The commissioners, with their surveyor, re-planned

the layout of the area to be enclosed. New roads and watercourses were made, plots of land were awarded to the parish for digging and quarrying road-making materials, and new plots of land were awarded to all those owners whose claims had been allowed, in lieu of their former scattered strip-holdings and rights of common; these plots were equal in value to the owner's former strips and common rights.

9.   The commissioners assessed the total cost of enclosure and apportioned these costs amongst all the people receiving land. The costs of hedging and fencing the new fields were excluded, and had to be met by the owners themselves.

10. The commissioners drew up a detailed summary of the results of enclosure. The changes were summarised in words and depicted on a detailed surveyor's plan. This document is known as the *enclosure award*, and represented the permanent legal record of the enclosure. With the execution of the award, the enclosure process was legally completed.

In East Yorkshire, the process of enclosure was rapidly carried forward from the third decade of the eighteenth century onwards. The first East Riding enclosure act was for Scagglethorpe, in 1725. Nearly fifty acts were passed in the peak decade, the 1770s, and there was an average of more than twenty in each decade between 1760 and 1820. By 1850, there had been 162 individual acts, and several more townships had made use of the General Enclosure Act passed after 1800. A few other enclosures were made by agreement, sometimes confirmed by an act. By these various means, some 250 townships were affected by enclosure in the years following 1725. The total area involved was extremely large. It has been estimated that, between 1725 and 1810, some 206,000 acres were enclosed on the Wolds, 68,000 acres in Holderness, and 44,000 acres in the Vale of York. Most of the later enclosures took place on the Wolds, and about 45,000 acres were dealt with in the period 1810-50. The last East Riding enclosure took place as recently as 1904, at Skipwith, in the Vale of York.

The above figures give a clear impression of the general transformation of the East Riding landscape during these years. However, at the level of the individual township, the scale of change was dependent upon the proportion of open field land involved. In some cases, there was so little old enclosure in a parish that the commissioners had almost unlimited scope. The enclosure of Wetwang in 1806, for example, dealt with 3,207 acres out of a total township acreage of 3,436. At the other end of the spectrum, there were townships, particularly in the Vale of York, where earlier enclosures had left only small areas for improvement. At North Duffield, for instance, only 1,106 acres of open fields and commons remained to be enclosed in 1814, out of the 3,417 acres of the township. A similar situation existed at Eastburn, to the west of Driffield, where most of the township had been enclosed in the later seventeenth century on the initiative of the then landowners, leaving only 440 acres of rabbit warren to be dealt with in 1849-50.

The enclosure commissioners, then, replaced each person's open field strips and common grazing rights with a number of fenced closes, grouped as far as practicable into discrete farm units. Both the commissioners and their surveyors worked to functional and

2. Typical Wolds enclosure landscape between Fimber and Fridaythorpe, created between 1806 and 1817.

efficient geometrical patterns, with new field boundaries paying little - if any - regard to previous landscape components. The typical parliamentary enclosure landscape is easily recognisable by its regular pattern of square or rectangular hedged fields, such as can still be seen, for example, between Driffield and Nafferton, to the north of the bypass. In general, however, the field pattern that we see today is not, of course, exactly that created by enclosure, for many of the large fields allotted by the commissioners were subsequently sub-divided. Sub-division has been particularly common on the Wolds, where large enclosure fields sometimes covered several hundred acres each. Even so, the fields of the Wolds, often covering 40 or 50 acres, are still generally larger than those of Holderness or the Vale of York. Over recent years, with the widespread grubbing-out of hedges, this trend to smallness has been somewhat reversed, and large, almost prairie-like, fields once again predominate in many districts.

Although ditches were utilised in the lower-lying, wetter, areas and stone walls were occasionally constructed on the Jurassic outcrop along the western edge of the Wolds, hedges were everywhere the usual means of demarcating field boundaries. Hedges were expensive. Initially, the plants had to be "brought up" under the temporary protection of underwood or posts and rails, and, in the general absence of suitable local timber, it was necessary to import large quantities of north European wood; locally, this was done through the ports at Bridlington and Hull. Also, the young hedges had to be protected from the predations of grazing animals, and the enclosure commissioners frequently prohibited sheep and other livestock from the fields for up to ten years after planting. Hawthorn was the most commonly used species for hedging, and, today, low thorn hedges are still one of the most enduring features of the East Riding landscape. Occasionally, other species were used, such as elder on the more exposed parts of the Wolds, or willow in especially wet places - in the Hull valley, for instance. And, more rarely, mixed hedges, rather than those composed of single species, were planted, as on the former common at Holme-upon-Spalding Moor.

Enclosure finally swept away not only the open fields but also the common pastures and wastes. While the commons themselves were replaced by a patchwork of regular fields, the access roads, known as outgangs, sometimes survive fossilised in today's landscape, as in the case of Carr Lane-Jilly Lane at Skidby, or as two wide trackways leaving the east end of the village green at Gembling.

Village greens, themselves, sometimes, but not commonly, fell victim to the enclosure process. Perhaps the best East Riding example of this process at work occurred at Harlthorpe, midway between Holme-upon-Spalding Moor and Selby. Here, in 1838, the enclosure commissioners divided the former green into hedged gardens and paddocks, and, as a result, the village houses now stand well back from the road.

On the porous chalklands the lack of surface water was a constant problem for past communities, and village wells, to take account of the fluctuating water-table, could be several hundred feet deep. Perhaps one of the most interesting, but, today, less commonly seen, features of the Wolds enclosure fields are the dew ponds, used for the watering of livestock. Dew ponds, for the collection of rain water, were shallow hollows dug into the chalk and then given a waterproof, usually a clay and lime, lining. Once constructed, they were, in the first instance, manually filled with water; there are occasional references, from the nineteenth and earlier twentieth centuries, to dew ponds having their water levels topped up by the dumping of waggon-loads of snow in them. Although these man-made livestock ponds could be constructed anywhere within the new fields, many were often placed along hedgelines so as to be inter-usable by animals in two or more adjoining fields. A good example of a dew pond straggling a hedge can be seen on the opposite side of the road to the Sir Tatton Sykes I Monument, between Garton-on-the-Wolds and Sledmere, beyond, and to the north of, the former Monument Keeper's cottage.

An equally common feature of the Wolds enclosure landscape are the small chalk quarries, many of which, now backfilled, are only visible as shallow craters, distinctively pockmarking field surfaces. These quarries, scattered across the fields, were dug in order to spread the extracted chalk rubble on to the field surfaces as a readily available means of supposedly improving the thin, leached, acidic soils. There is no evidence to suggest that this technique had any real effect, and, as the nineteenth century progressed, it was replaced by commercially available products, such as guano and crushed bone. Seams of marl within the chalk were also exploited and spread on the land as a means of soil improvement.

Today, the East Riding countryside has a well-wooded appearance. The origins of much of this woodland, whether it was planted for the aesthetic enhancement of the landscaped parks surrounding the houses of the landed gentry, for its commercial potential, or for the benefit of its protective qualities in exposed locations, are to be found in the enclosure years, especially on the Wolds. Plantations of Scotch pine, spruce, larch, beech and ash were established across the face of the region - as shelter belts surrounding and protecting exposed farmsteads and fringing exposed fields, as coverts for foxes and game-birds, as shelter for sheep, or for profit on steep, otherwise unproductive, valley sides. Large acreages could be involved: for instance, by the beginning of the twentieth century, 870 acres at Sledmere, out of a total township area of 7,000 acres, had been given over to woodland. This pattern was repeated over much of the Wolds and, to a lesser extent, in Holderness and the Vale of York.

One of the more enduring legacies of enclosure is the modern road network. Many of our present-day roads owe their existence to these years, when the enclosure commissioners took the opportunity to straighten or realign older routeways. Frequently, old roads were blocked and new ones laid out as part of the general landscape rationalisation. The road between Garton-on-the-Wolds and Sledmere, straight and wide, is a typical example.

The wholesale reorganisation of the landscape brought about by enclosure is, perhaps, nowhere better seen than in the establishment of new farmsteads. Where each farmer's land had previously been scattered amongst the open fields, enclosure resulted in the formation of compact farms. For the first time, each farmer now had his land together at one point in the landscape, and, in very many cases, the opportunity was taken to move out of the villages and build new farmhouses and ranges of buildings on these new holdings. In the process, hundreds of new farmsteads were created across the landscape, giving the countryside a much more lived in appearance; for instance, the enclosure of Flamborough in 1767 resulted, in the following years, in the construction of ten outlying farms, or at Bainton, where, following the 1775 enclosure, six new farmsteads were built at various locations across the township.

3. Enclosure landscape at Aldro on the western Wolds, dating to c.1766, with Birdsall House surrounded by its parkland in the middle distance. Aldro Farm *(bottom left)* shows a continuous sequence of development from the early nineteenth century to the present: in 1810, the farm buildings were grouped around a foldyard, with the house immediately to the south, and a dew pond slightly to the east of the complex; by 1850, a larger range, enclosing a second foldyard, had been added immediately to the north of the earlier yard, and a separate implement shed, barn and granary had also been constructed, perhaps reflecting a change from pastoral to arable farming; by 1890, a west range of farm buildings had been constructed and the pond relocated to the west of the 1850 foldyard; by 1900, the main yards were covered, and shelter belts had been planted around the farmstead; and, throughout the twentieth century, new ranges of buildings were added: a dutch barn, cattle yard, sheep houses, and grain stores.

Indeed, a present-day journey across any part of the East Riding cannot fail to notice the existence of isolated, enclosure farmsteads, many nestling within protective shelter belts.

This movement away from existing centres of population brought about, for the first time, the creation of purpose-built, co-ordinated ranges of farm buildings. Prior to enclosure, farm buildings had usually been built, rebuilt and added to in an *ad hoc* manner, sometimes with a construction history stretching back over several centuries. With the onset of enclosure, from the late eighteenth century onwards, farm design, involving the deliberate arrangement of buildings in a regular and convenient layout, became commonplace. Now, in East Yorkshire, as in most other areas of England, new farmsteads were constructed around a central, square, foldyard, with adjoining barns, stables and cattle houses. In 1788, agriculturalist William Marshall provided a short description of farmsteads then being built on the Wolds:

Dwelling-house to the west; barns and stable on the north; stack-hovels, for cattle and implements, on the east; the whole forming a square straw-yard, open to the south, saving a high brick wall, with tall boarded gates.

A little later the same writer produced a more extended description, highlighting the variety of layout in the new farmsteads:

The particular requirements of a farmstead are as various as the intention of farms. A sheep farm, a grazing farm, a hay farm, a dairy farm and one under mixed cultivation require different situations and different arrangements of yards and buildings. The basic requirements are a suite of buildings, adapted to the intended plan of management, as a dwelling house, barns, stables, cattlesheds and cart-shed. All these are to be united by a spacious yard, common to the buildings, and containing a receptacle of stall-manure, whether arising from the stables, cattlesheds, hogsties, or other buildings; together with separate folds, or straw yards, furnished with appropriate sheds, for particular stock, in places where such are required. Liquid manure should be collected in a reservoir or catchpool, situated on the lower side of the buildings and yards, to receive their washings, and collect them in a body for the purposes of irrigating the lands below them. There should be a corn-yard, convenient to the barns, a hay-barn contiguous to the cow or fattening sheds and a garden and orchard near the house. Also, there should be a grass-yard or green, embracing the whole or principal part of the conveniences, as an occasional receptacle for stock of every kind, as a common pasture for swine, and a range of poultry, and as an ante-field or lobby, out of which the home grounds and driftways may conveniently be entered.

Technological advancement was reflected in the design and construction of new farm buildings. For example, with the invention of the threshing machine in the late eighteenth century, and the harnessing of horse power to drive it, sheds were built onto barns in order to accommodate horse-wheels. Power generated from horse-wheels was used not only for threshing, but for turnip-chopping, cake-crushing, straw-cutting, and oat-rolling, as well as for a range of other activities. Most surviving wheel-houses - and there are few - are single-storeyed structures, sometimes square but more frequently six- or seven-sided. On the more affluent farms, horse-power was gradually replaced by the static steam engine, reflected in the construction of engine houses and tall chimneys.

A common feature of the larger Wolds farms was the presence of one or more subsidiary farmsteads. Often located on the higher and more remote parts of a farm, these additional units usually comprised a small foldyard and barn, occasionally with an attached cottage, and frequently took the name 'High Barn' or 'Wold Barn'. These ranges, perched on exposed wold tops, were primarily intended for the over-wintering of cattle; subsequently, the deposits of manure which had accumulated in the foldyards were, as an aid to soil fertility, spread over the surrounding arable land. This practice obviated the time-consuming need to get dung carts from the main farmstead up on to the higher wold land. Many of the high barns have disappeared over the last fifty or so years, and many others are now in a derelict state. Disused examples can still be seen at Towthorpe, near Fimber, and in the Birdsall-Wharram Percy area.

Farm size varied considerably across the East Riding. By far the largest holdings were located on the Wolds, with typical acreages of between 600-800 acres, but, in some cases, in excess of 1,000 acres. These farms attracted a special kind of farmer. Because of the large acreages involved, tenants had to be men of capital, and, accordingly, came from a different kind of social background when compared with the majority of farmers elsewhere in the region. As a group, they valued education and were progressive in their outlook. Francis Jordan, the tenant at Eastburn, may be cited as fairly typical of this class of farmer. When he took over the 1,300 acre holding in 1849, he invested around £8,000 of his own capital in a major series of improvements, including the erection of two new farmstead complexes (at Eastburn and Eastburn Warren).

4. Eastburn Warren Farm, built 1849-50 by Francis Jordan at a total cost of £2,430 2s.11d., on the site of the former rabbit warren. The farm house is to the right, or south, of the farm buildings, which are arranged around two central foldyards, the whole surrounded by a shelter belt. In 1869, the farm was described as:

The north side of [the] *buildings consists of a lofty barn and granaries, which protect two large foldyards. These yards are shedded all round, the sheds having cribs beneath them. As the yards adjoin, the sheds down the centre are placed back to back; and here we find the turnip and cake houses, and other convenient offices. Stabling for 18 horses is provided on the outside of the eastern yard.*

Throughout the nineteenth century, Eastburn Warren was a 466-acre arable unit; in more recent times, it has functioned as a pig unit belonging to JSR Farms Ltd., Southburn.

Although there were notable exceptions (eg Haverfield Farm, Patrington), lowland farm sizes were much smaller, with holdings of between 100-400 acres tending to be the norm.

Along with enclosure, new crops appeared. For the first time, farmers, freed from the constraints of the communal regulations governing the operation and management of the open fields, were able to make their own individual decisions and choices. The introduction of turnips and clover, sainfoin and grass, made it possible to use improved crop rotations and methods of livestock management. Although there were many variations to suit different soil types and conditions, a four-course rotation was widely adopted: turnips-barley-grass/clover-wheat. Large numbers of sheep and cattle, essential for their manure, were also kept on the new farms. Overall, the emphasis was on providing produce for the market, not the subsistence requirements of the farmer and his family, and, as the nineteenth century progressed, agriculture became more and more integrated into the emerging capitalist economy, taking its place alongside textiles, coal, shipbuilding, and a host of other industries, as a profit-making business enterprise.

Enclosure dramatically transformed the appearance of the countryside, inscribing yet another layer of man-made modification on to a landscape which had seen generation after generation of change over the previous 8,000 years. But what of the human dimension? As with most things in life, there were both winners and losers. Enclosure was expensive, and the costs had to be shared, proportionately, by all those who acquired land under the process. Some simply could not afford to pay their share, and were bought out by the more affluent. This created a vast army of dispossessed former landholders, individuals effectively divorced from their livelihood. Stark choices had to be made. In reality, most stayed on the land, becoming wage-labourers on the new farms; others became involved in the developing agricultural service industries, as blacksmiths, wheelwrights, ropemakers, and so on; and yet others migrated to the new industrial centres, to the towns of West Yorkshire or the North-East, where they became industrial workers.

6. The Sledmere estate

5. Portrait of Sir Christopher, 2nd. Baronet, and Lady Sykes of Sledmere by George Romney, 1793.

The origins of the modern Sledmere landscape can be traced to 1748, when Richard Sykes (1706-61) inherited the nucleus of what was to become, in the later nineteenth century, the 34,010 acre agricultural estate, from his uncle Mark Kirby.

In 1751, Sykes began the construction of a new mansion to replace the existing Tudor manor house, surrounding it with parkland, and, in the process, began the piecemeal removal of the old village, from its site in front of the new house, to its present position; as the parkland was progressively enlarged in later decades, the remainder of the village was relocated.

Sir Christopher Sykes (1749-1801) was responsible for further improvements to the house, for laying out the rest of the Sledmere landscape, and for continuing the family tradition of buying large amounts of land on the Wolds. With monies from inheritances and from borrowing, Sykes, in the thirty years between 1771 and 1801, spent over £180,000 on the purchasing of 18,000 acres, its enclosure and improvement, and on the building of farmsteads. Most of this land was on the northern Wolds and formed a consolidated block centred on Sledmere, but also included outlying portions in Holderness.

In 1775-76, against some initial opposition, he enclosed the 7,043 acre parish, establishing the landscape much as it is seen today. The parkland was extended and remodelled to include avenues, belts and clumps of trees, creating a fluid composition with sinuous boundaries. Altogether, around 1,000 acres of Scots pine, larch, spruce, beech, wild cherry, ash, holly and quickwood were planted. Between 1771 and 1801, Sykes spent £20,547 12s. 3½d. on improvements to the house and its immediate surroundings.

In addition, Sir Christopher transformed the parish by the construction of eight new farmsteads, three of which - Marramatte, Life Hill and Castle - stand out as being cleverly integrated into the parkland landscape: they were sited in highly specific locations so as to function as distinctive eye-catching features when viewed from the house. The other farms, ranging in size from 44 to 650 acres, were: Avenue Farm, Croome Farm, Croome House Farm, Mill Farm, and Wood Hill Farm.

The portrait by Romney shows, in the background and to the right, the elements of the new landscape at Sledmere, with both Sir Christopher and Lady Sykes' outstretched arms and hands drawing the viewer's attention to the achievements of this period: in descending order, a new farmstead (possibly Marramatte) surrounded by its shelter belt, enclosed fields, and parkland.

Sir Christopher died on 17 September 1801, whilst taking the waters at Hotwells, near Bristol. His obituary in the **Gentleman's Magazine** commented on his achievements:

... he has left an excellent character in every relation of life, whether public or private, and was, in every sense of the word, an enlightened country gentleman. His early rising and great activity ... prompted the conduct of every plan of amending the state of the country, whether by drainage or inclosure, building or navigation; and his improvements extended themselves over a surface of near 100 miles. The wolds of Yorkshire, where he had property, will be his lasting monument.

Locally, Sykes' achievements are commemorated in two physical monuments. The first, a wall tablet, erected by his eldest daughter Decima Foulis, is in the chancel of West Heslerton church. Echoing the eulogistic sentiments expressed in the above quoted obituary, the inscription records that:

Every plan of improving the general state and surface of the country, either by Enclosure, Drainage, Building, or Navigation found him an active friend and supporter; in fact in every sense of the word he proved himself a most enlightened country gentleman ... Whoever now traverses the wolds of Yorkshire, and contrasts their present appearance with what they were, cannot fail to extol the name of Sykes ...

The second monument, erected in 1840 by his son, the then Sir Tatton I, consists of an ornamental well, opposite the Lodges at the entrance to Sledmere House. It bears the inscription:

This edifice was erected by Sir Tatton Sykes Bart. to the memory of his father Sir Christopher Sykes Bart., who by assiduity and perseverance in building and planting and inclosing the Yorkshire Wolds, in the short space of thirty years, set such an example to other owners of land, as has caused what was once a bleak and barren tract of country to become now one of the most productive and best cultivated districts in the County of York.

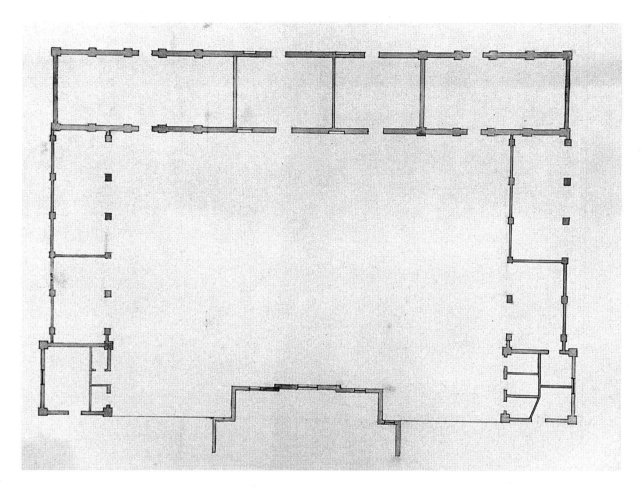

6. Plan of Marramatte Farm Sledmere, c.1775-78, attributed to Sir Christopher Sykes. The plan shows the integrated layout of a new post-enclosure farmstead, constructed around a central foldyard. The suites of buildings were arranged in such a way as to allow ease of movement and an integrated flow of processes. Thus, at the rear, there was stabling, opening directly into the foldyard, with granary, and hayloft over, and a barn, situated in the centre of the range. On the right, there are shelter sheds opening into the foldyard, whilst on the left a cart shed, adjoining the stable, faces into what was the stackyard. The pavilions, at lower left and right, functioned as poultry houses and pigsties. The farmstead was built c.1778-79.

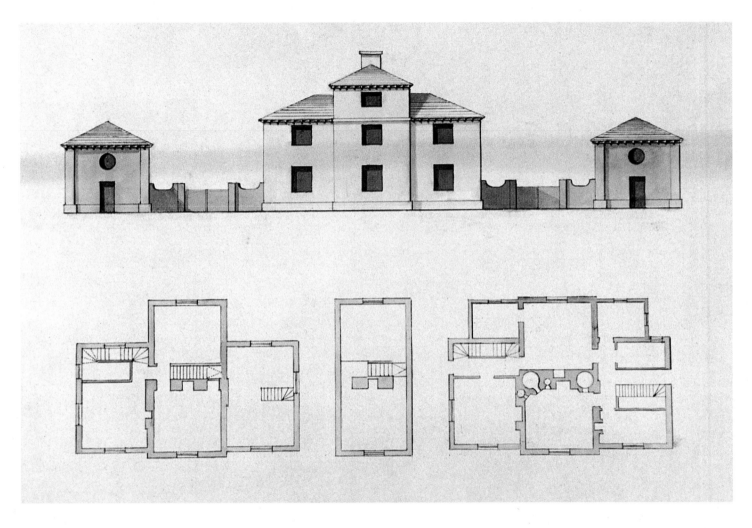

7. South-facing elevation of Marramatte Farm, c.1775-78, attributed to Sir Christopher Sykes. The view intended to be seen from Sledmere House, one mile to the east. Note the imposing facade and its symmetrical arrangement, with a centrally-positioned house and its three-storey central block, projecting high walls to left and right, behind which the working farmstead is obscured, and which end in pavilions.

8. Marramatte Farm, 1999, from the south-west, showing south-facing front of the house with farm buildings to the north.

9. South-facing elevation and plan of Life Hill farm house, Sledmere, c.1775-78, attributed to Sir Christopher Sykes, and which was constructed c.1778-79. This is the view intended to be seen from Sledmere House, some one and a half miles to the north. Note the similarities and differences in design between Marramatte Farm and Life Hill Farm.

10. Life Hill Farm, 1999, from the south, showing the rear of the house and farm buildings set around the foldyard

11. West-facing front of Castle Farm, Sledmere, built c.1778-79, and attributed to the architect John Carr of York. Like both Marramatte and Life Hill, it was strategically placed in the landscape so as to be visible from Sledmere House, one mile to the west. Note the contrast with the other two farmsteads: a Gothic gatehouse, pointed arched entrance flanked by projecting octagonal towers, a mixture of square-headed and pointed two-light windows with tracery and hoodmoulds, and finished with battlements at roof level. To left and right are projecting wings, which originally formed part of the functional farm buildings arranged around a foldyard immediately to the east of the house. During the nineteenth and twentieth centuries, the Castle has variously served as a home for the Sledmere agent and as a working farmstead.

12. Portrait photograph of Sir Tatton Sykes I (1772-1863), 4th. Baronet.

Sir Tatton Sykes I - *T'au'd Squire*, as he was popularly known - succeeded to the Sledmere estate on the death of his elder brother Mark, the 3rd. Baronet, in 1823. Unfortunately, this was at a time of

severe agricultural depression, which saw a period of retrenchment at Sledmere, including the selling off of large amounts of land. However, with the return of agricultural prosperity, in the 1840s and 1850s, Sir Tatton, following in the family tradition, embarked on a policy of expansion. Land was bought, further consolidating the holdings on the northern Wolds, so much so that by 1873 the estate consisted of 34,010 acres. At this time, owing to improvements and careful management, Sledmere ranked, after Holkham in Norfolk, as the premier agricultural estate in eastern England.

Sir Tatton died on 21 March 1863, aged ninety years, and was buried at Sledmere, his coffin being carried from the house to the church by twelve estate workers. Following his death, one of his obituarists summed up, in suitably elegaic language, Sir Tatton's achievements:

In truth he was a missionary in his way, and one of an uncommonly rare and useful sort. We must remember that Providence placed him in an inheritance of several square miles of Yorkshire wolds ... The Yorkshire wolds are not, strictly speaking, a romantic, nor even an inviting part of England. They consist, or consisted in Sir Tatton's early days, of a bare, treeless, waterless table-land, some thirty miles square, fit for nothing but sheep-walks, and hardly maintaining a sheep to an acre, and possessing the solitary advantage that you might gallop twenty miles "on end" without being troubled with a fence. They were dotted here and there with an uncouth village ... its straight street and straggling row of houses, and its dilapidated church - a pond at one end of the place for the cattle and geese of the community, and perhaps a few fir trees round the two or three chief farmsteads - and then broad undulating chalk downs for miles and miles, and then another village, painfully like the last. This was Sir Tatton's Sparta. He owned, perhaps, a quarter of the whole district, and nothing could look more dreary than his inheritance. But he was exactly the man for the place. With infinite pains and cost he raised a splendid breed of sheep; and from his training ground and its 120 brood mares came many hundreds of the best hunters in the country, and many of our best racers. The high prices of the war, his unstinted application of capital, and the enterprising set of tenants that his reputation gathered around him, enabled him (with the help of his favourite "bones" manure) to turn bare sheep walks into rich corn-growing land, averaging from forty to forty-eight bushels of wheat to the acre, enclosed by fences of his own devising, and many of them planted by his own hand. The valleys were well wooded with miles of plantations, every farm was well furnished with reservoirs after a plan of his own, and with some of the best farm buildings in England, and finally (we must not forget to add) tilled by a population paid and fed in a way that would make ... poor Dorsetshire proteges wish to emigrate thither at once. All this was achieved long ago; his farms have been models for nearly half a century. Latterly, also - for to the very end he kept pace with the times he lived in - he took to school founding and church building. Every village on his estate has now a good school, and the Wold churches are on a level with those of our richest districts. His latest work of this kind, erected as a memorial to his wife, and consecrated about a year ago, is one of the most beautiful village churches imaginable [Bishop Wilton] ...

Following Sir Tatton's death, a local committee, under the chairmanship of Lord Hotham, was established in order to raise monies for the provision of a lasting memorial to his memory. This fund, subscribed to *by his tenantry and numerous friends, in testimony of his worth and the esteem in which he was held by all who had the privilege of knowing his many virtues in all the relations of life as parent, friend or landlord*, raised £1,916 5s.4d.

The committee promoted a national design competition for the most fitting memorial. Out of 157 submissions, the winning entry was by the Oxford-based architect John Gibbs. Gibbs' design consisted of a:

monumental cross 120 feet high and 28 feet in diameter at the base. It is composed of Whitby and Mansfield stone, the columns and strings being of the same material. The chief stage is devoted to sculpture, in which is represented characteristically the late baronet, also coat of arms, devices, foliage in caps, cornices, and strings, with ornamental ironwork. For a considerable height the column is hollow, and a staircase is provided, at the top of which is a room, lighted by four three-light windows. The memorial is a fine conception of the early decorated period, the ornamental portion, which is very limited, being judiciously arranged to give the greatest effect for the amount of sculpture. Over the doorway Sir Tatton is represented engaged in one of his favourite pursuits - hunting.

The monument was deliberately sited in a prominent topographical location, on Garton Hill, mid-way between the villages of Sledmere and Garton-on-the-Wolds. This particular site was chosen not only because:

it is in immediate contiguity with the the locality which was long the residence of the individual whose memory the monument was desired to perpetuate, but also because it was a situation from which it could be seen at a greater distance than any other spot in the neighbourhood which could have been fixed upon for the purpose.

The foundation stone was laid on 17 May 1865 by Lord Hotham. The monument, built by Messrs. Simpson and Malone of Hull, was completed during the summer of 1866, and the official opening ceremony, performed by Lord Hotham, took place on 26 October that year:

Long before the hour fixed for the commencement of proceedings - 12 noon - large numbers of visitors from the neighbouring villages and from long distances, comprising the leading aristocracy of the Riding, had repaired to the scene to inspect the monument ... The inauguration had been looked forward to with great interest for a considerable time ... The morning dawned with a cloudless sky, and save that the road was heavy for pedestrians (who lined the road the whole distance from Driffield to the monument), the weather was all that could be desired. The scene at the inauguration was a very pleasing one, there being close upon 500 people present, including the elite of the Riding, and many from a distance.

Today, standing stark against the skyline, the Victorian Gothic monument, representing a highly visible past, dominates the local landscape, and serves to enhance the significance of a particular locality and its history, providing a commentary on the agricultural changes which affected this part of the East Riding during the nineteenth century.

13. Inauguration ceremony of the monument to commemorate the memory of Sir Tatton Sykes I, 26 October 1866.

7. *The hiring fairs*

The previous chapter examined the profound structural changes wrought on the East Yorkshire landscape as a result of the parliamentary enclosure movement of the eighteenth and nineteenth centuries. To contemporary observers, enclosure was the most visible and dramatic aspect of the economic revolution in agriculture, altering the form of the countryside. Essentially, the modern rural landscape of trim fields, separated by hedges and ditches, surrounding compact, isolated farmsteads was in the process of formation in the decades after c.1730. Once put in place, it was a structure that remained largely unaltered until into the twentieth century. Over time, virtually all traces of the old agriculture, and the ancient social structure associated with it, were removed.

Enclosure not only transformed the physical appearance of the countryside, but also heralded, in particular, new social and economic relationships among, and between, different sections of the rural population. The emphasis in this and the next chapter will be on the structure of the agricultural labour force, focusing on the tenor and rhythm of life.

Throughout the nineteenth and earlier part of the twentieth centuries, the East Riding agricultural workforce consisted of four distinct categories:

1. Farmers and their male relatives working on the farm. This group consisted of two main sub-categories: (i) owner-occupiers, generally farming under 300 acres, and (ii) tenants, holding their farms from one or other of the landed estates, and farming around 400-500 acres, but sometimes up to 1,200 or 1,300 acres, and throughout the nineteenth century accounting for approximately 90% of all farmers. Generally innovative and progressive, usually highly capitalised and well-resourced, both these groups, employing large workforces, were producing for the market, whether it be livestock or grain or a range of other saleable commodities. These were the great capitalist farmers of the Victorian period. In addition, there was a small, but significant, number of what some historians term 'peasant producers' - that is, small farmers, usually holding considerably less than 50 acres of land, perhaps drawing their workforce entirely from the family, and who were farming at subsistence levels, almost exclusively producing for their own needs. Collectively, in the mid-nineteenth century, East Riding farmers and their families accounted for approximately 24% of the total agricultural workforce.

2. Farm servants: unmarried lads and young men, who were hired and paid by the year, and who, as part of their pay, received board and lodging on the farmstead. In return for his pay and keep, the farm servant, as his title implies, placed himself at the farmer's disposal, working as required for a whole year, within boundaries set by reason and customary practice. In the 1850s, this group formed 33% of the total East Riding agricultural workforce.

3. Agricultural labourers: married workers who were

paid by the day or by the week, or, at harvest time, by piece-work. Agricultural labourers formed the most numerous group of East Riding farm workers, accounting for 43% of the total agricultural workforce in the mid-nineteenth century; and

4.   Casual labourers: workers, including women and children, who were hired at particularly busy times during the annual agricultural cycle - eg sheep shearing, cereal harvest, potato harvest - to supplement the permanent workforce. Typically, these were migrant workers coming, in the case of the East Riding, from the Yorkshire Dales or Ireland. Although not noted for their keenness to work, the well-known Wolds Rangers - tramps living rough in the local countryside - also formed part of the casual agricultural workforce, and were a frequent sight in the area up to the 1960s. Casual labourers were paid by piece-work, known locally as *tacking it ba'tack*. Given the fluctuating nature of this group, it is not possible to estimate the number of people involved.

In many respects, the farm servants - the horse lads as they were commonly known - formed the agricultural elite. Following enclosure, many new farmsteads were built in isolated locations, away from existing settlements. The relative geographical isolation of these farmsteads, *so scattered and so separated from the rest of the world* in the words of one contemporary commentator, created problems in relation to securing an adequate workforce. This was overcome by the adoption of the practice of boarding unmarried workers - the farm servants - on the steading itself, either in the farmhouse or, more commonly, with the hind (foreman) and his family. Local evidence presented to the 1867-68 **Royal Commission on the Employment of Children, Young Persons, and Women in Agriculture** drew attention to this system:

Where as in the East Riding of Yorkshire the farms are large and very detached, the farmer's house is like a barrack with a long chamber full of beds, one of which the foreman commonly occupies to keep order.

In evidence presented to the 1881 **Royal Commission on the Depressed State of the Agricultural Interest**, this theme was again taken up, but, by this date, servants were now normally boarded in separate quarters, in the hind's house:

Day labourers are scarce and often reside at long distances from the farm; hence the system of hiring team and cattle men by the year is universal, and barracks under the eye of the hind, who is practically their master, are necessary. Formerly the hired servants boarded at the tenant's house, and were more immediately under his control and supervision; but on large occupations this practice has given way to boarding in the hind's house.

Farm servants were set apart from other agricultural workers in that they were hired for a year at a time and were subject to legally enforceable contracts of employment. In the East Riding, farm servants' contracts ran from one Old Martinmas Day (23 November) to the next. These workers found employment through the annual statute hirings, which were held in the market towns of the region during Martinmas week, in Beverley, Bridlington, Driffield, Hedon, Hornsea, Howden, Hull, Hunmanby, Malton, Market Weighton,

Patrington, Pocklington, Scarborough, Selby, and York. Here the agricultural servants, male as well as female, would gather in order to bargain with prospective employers, and, hopefully, secure a position for the coming year.

Local newspapers carried detailed reports of these colourful, and sometimes rowdy, gatherings. For instance, the **Driffield Times**, in its 15 November 1873 issue, captures the early morning atmosphere of that year's hirings in the town:

Early in the morning the great stream of humanity rolled into the town, conveyed thither in every conceivable appliance that could be obtained for the occasion; but conspicuous among the rest were the heavy waggons with their living freight, which were deposited amid the greetings of those who had chanced to outstrip them in the drive to town. Other vehicles, from heavy waggons to the humble donkey and cart were to be seen threading their way through the streets to their several destinations. The Railway Company, too, brought hundreds into the town by special and regular trains, which were literally packed. At about nine o'clock the bustle was commenced in earnest, for by that time most of the servants had congregated ...

The unfolding events of hiring day can be glimpsed from a later report of the Bridlington hirings. The following extract, from the 16 November 1895 issue of the **Bridlington Gazette**, conveys the scene with all the clarity and vividness of a photographic image:

Everyone tried to look smart ... If a masher, you will see him in a light salmon-coloured moleskin jacket with black velvet collar, and a pair of smart corduroys, velvet coloured, perhaps, and split up at the bottoms, with rows of pearlies on either side. The waggoner has

a bit of fancifully twisted cord in his cap, a bright flower (it may be artificial) in his buttonhole, and his jacket is not buttoned - that would not be correct. The proper fastening is two or three inches of brass chain, the better to display a capacious chest. Feathers on some of the bowler hats are suggestive of the fold-yard ... If you were a horseman you had a bit of horse-hair in your coat collar, and if you were a shepherd you had a bit o'wool. If you were a cowman you had a bit of hair out o'cow tail.

The actual process whereby an individual was hired is demonstrated in the following extract of oral testimony:

We lined ourselves up on one side of t'road and farmers on t'other. They looked you over, talked to one another, and asked each other if they knew you and what you were like. They'd discuss you among themselves. Then they'd come across and say, "Noo, lad, dos't thoo want takin' on?"

If a bargain was struck, the farmer would seal the transaction by giving the hired lad or man fest , or fastening, money - a small sum - in recognition of the hiring. The amount of fest money varied: locally, in the late nineteenth and early twentieth centuries, usually 5s. for a wagoner, and 2s.6d. for other workers.

What form did the contract take? The actual conditions of work were never explicitly stated during the negotiations, and much was governed by custom, a practice that was common amongst farm servants in other areas of Britain. The contracts themselves were predominantly oral. The few written contracts that were obtained rarely specified more than the wage and termination date, as in the following handwritten example, drawn up on 25 October 1897, between Francis Johnson, farmer at Brigham House House Farm, and Samuel Ellwood:

I Samuel Ellwood engage to Mr Francis Johnson as waggoner from Martinmas 1897 to Martinmas 1898 for £19 - nineteen pounds.
[Signed] Samuel Ellwood

Therefore, a whole range of employment conditions were subject to 'implicit', informal agreement, that both worker and farmer assumed were automatically part of the labour agreement. These included hours of work, holidays, sick pay, and occupational and hierarchical divisions of labour on the farm. Part of the implicit contract entered into between farmers and hired hands at Driffield and Malton was that the servants would have their respective town's show-day off work.

Once the fest money had changed hands, a legally binding contract had been entered into, and it is not uncommon to find reports of farmers taking hired workers to a police court or county court for breaching this contract, either for not turning up at all or for leaving the farm before the contract had expired. If either party withdrew before the year was up, magistrates and judges had special powers to enforce the contract, or to award damages for breach of contract. Wages due could only be claimed before the year was over if a breach of contract by the farmer could be proved, but the farmer could not recover his spending on board and lodging in any circumstances.

The newspaper reports of hirings also contain information on the annual wages paid in the districts to which they relate. For example, at the Malton Hirings of 1874, the following details can be found in the **Malton Messenger** of 14 November:

The hirings were held on Tuesday, when the number of servants - male and female - was very large. The wages for girls from 12 to 18 years, ranged from £6 to £12; upper servants and housekeepers from £13 to £15. Boys from 13 to 15 years old, from £10 to £12; those from 16 to 18, from £18 to £20. Good shepherds and experienced foremen asked and obtained from £20 to £30 [and] some were engaged at even a much higher rate.

In the same year, the **Driffield Times**, in its 14 November issue, reported wage rates for agricultural servants in the area around the town as:

Young foremen £25; experienced foremen, £30, and in a few instances £32 and £33; young waggoners £18; experienced waggoners £20; strong plough boys from £13 to £15; young maids-of-all-work obtained £9 to £12; housemaids £12 to £14; experienced cooks £20.

The essential point about the hirings was that wage rates were fixed locally, and were dependent upon local conditions at particular points in time. In the emerging capitalist economy, they were reliant upon such factors as the general state of agriculture - in good years, wages were high, and, in lean years, they were driven down - and supply and demand.

In relation to wages, it is also important to point out that, with the exception of any subs advanced during the year, they were paid annually, at the termination of the contract. The agricultural servant's wage was divided equally between a cash payment and his keep. For example, a typical East Riding wagoner's annual wage in 1900 was £25 5s. in cash (ie £25 *plus* 5s. fest money) and £25 board and lodging, giving total earnings of £50 5s.

To contemporaries, particularly to the cultured middle classes, the annual agricultural hirings were iniquitous, degrading and inhuman affairs, where agricultural servants were herded together *like so many cattle open for inspection*. In general, these events were characterised by rowdyism and drunkness, and, on occasions, by serious disturbances. As the **Driffield Times** of November 15 1873 reported of the town's hirings five days previously:

... One could hardly imagine we were living in the nineteenth century to see so much that appeared to be almost worse than heathenism. Directly a sufficient quantity of aqua vitæ had been imbibed loquaciousness was the result, and most disgustingly abusive language soon found sequence in blows. Long before mid-day was reached several rather severe hand-to-hand struggles took place, the combatants in many instances receiving extensive wounds on the head, and "black eyes" were also visible upon the physiognomy of numbers of women as well as men. Later in the day we actually heard that knives had been drawn by a determined couple of desperadoes, and the result might have been somewhat serious, had they not been separated by the police.

Or, to quote a second example, as the **East and North Riding Chronicle**, in its edition of 13 November 1875, reported of the Bridlington hirings of that year:

A great disturbance took place ... between police and farm servants. During the afternoon, a young man who was drunk made a disturbance. He was taken to the police-station, and several of his mates set on the policemen and kicked and knocked them about ... There were only a few policemen in the town, and they were quite unable to repress the rioters, who for a long time had it their own way.

The general tenor of the disturbances can be gauged from a letter, exhibiting a degree of class antagonism and also hinting at the growing separation between town and country that was taking place at this time, which appeared in the correspondence column of the **Driffield Times**, also on 13 November 1875, reflecting on that year's hirings in the town:

Sir, - Last Friday, the 5th. Nov., the town was given up to the licence and riot of unruly lads with fireworks; and the peaceful inhabitants have hardly recovered from their annoyance when the streets are once more abandoned to a lawless mob of roughs from the country, who according to custom flocked into the town on the pretence of selling their labour for the ensuing year. For years statute hirings have been a disgrace to the civilisation of the East Riding on moral grounds; they are now rapidly becoming insufferable on social ones. What justification has the farming interest for expecting that townspeople should uncomplainingly yield up their comfort, their convenience, their streets, and their footpaths, to perpetuate the evil custom of agricultural roughs assembling to sell their labour in the open market? The rule which applies to the better class of female servants applies with equal force to male servants. If there is a respectable housekeeper, cook, or housemaid, in a farm-house she is hired privately, either personally or by letter. Why should not the foreman, or the waggoner, or the plough lad be engaged in the same way? Anyhow, it rests with farmers and landholders to find out some way of relieving towns from the disgraceful orgies witnessed each succeeding November.

It is idle to argue that the rough untutored agricultural servants assemble for purposes. The main object is boisterous horseplay arising out of drinking, varied perhaps with a little rioting and fighting. If they can get hired before this object is attained, well and good; but this is subordinate to the holiday element. Employers of labour find this to be the case, and admit it; for unless they can engage servants early in the day, before they find their way to the public-houses, they find them so saucy and independent that engagements are impossible. Unaccustomed to self-restraint, self-control, or proper respect for their betters, it would surely be desirable to transact business with them before they are excited or muddled with pints of beer.

The police have been known to decline to arrest men who have committed breaches of the peace under their immediate observation, flatly declaring they dared not do so; thus shewing our present police system utterly inadequate to deal with the nuisance.

The riot (for it was nothing less) which took place last Monday afternoon was utterly indefensible. We are told a lad was struck for some offence by a man performing in a booth (we are not told if the man received any, or what provocation); having assaulted the lad, the offender should have been handed over to the nearest policeman, who would doubtless have taken the stranger into custody: instead of which the roughs lawlessly seized the occasion to demolish the booth, destroy its contents, and grievously maltreat the owners - holding possession of the Market-place during their pleasure, various shops closing their windows for safety.

Another episode:- A man is standing by two policemen; he is suddenly attacked by five or six men (not lads); he defends himself as best he can, in the presence of the policemen, ultimately seeking shelter in the shop of Mr. Meek, where he is followed by his pursuers, where their game is concluded by assaulting Mr. Meek's son for trying to protect the shop window, and then rushing into the house, dangerously alarming the wife of Mr. Meek.

The day has been well spent if it is the means of driving another nail into the coffin in which it is the interest of peaceable householders to see buried - statute hirings!

I am, Sir, A HOUSEHOLDER

Other evils attendant upon the hirings, as hinted at in the above, were pointed to by many contemporaries: the prevalence of pickpockets, the bad language, and *the miserable enticements of the Penny Theatres with objectionable scenes.* The hired servants spent their fest money, and more, on wild beast shows, conjurors' booths, shooting galleries, strength testers, electrical machines, quack doctors, and the public houses, which they frequented *for want of anywhere else to go.* Drunken orgies had *consequences which may be guessed.*

Throughout the second half of the nineteenth century, popular pamphlets, such as those written in 1854 by the Rev. John Eddowes, vicar of Garton-on-the-Wolds, railed against the hirings. In **Martinmas Musings** and **The Agricultural Labourer As He Really Is**, Eddowes likened hiring day to a slave market. Newspaper editorials, adopting a high moral, religiously-inspired, tone also fulminated against these events, and called for their outright abolition. To such people, it was clear that the leading role in ending the hirings must come from the educated and socially-responsible upper and middle classes. An editorial in the 16 November 1872 issue of the **Malton Messenger**, illustrative of the general feeling at the time, was in no doubt that:

The remedy for this annual evil, must to our minds, come not from the lower class but from those above them, and it is high time that some serious movement was originated to stop this barbarous and soul-endangering system.

Despite numerous campaigns throughout the nineteenth century, the annual hirings persisted through to the mid-1940s. Between c.1914 and their end in 1946, the hirings gradually became less frequent as other means of employing labour became the norm. The ending of the system was caused by a number of developments: the progressive and dramatic decline in the number of working horses, which provided the rationale for the hiring system, and the concomitant rise in agricultural mechanisation; the decline in the number of farm workers; the introduction of standard wage rates from the 1920s onwards; the institutionalisation of agrarian trades unionism; and, within the context of the fragmentation of traditional rural communities and the dissolution of the rigidly hierarchical social structure that was Victorian and Edwardian Britain, a general unwillingness on the part of unmarried farm workers to subject themselves any longer to an outmoded and outdated set of employment practices.

Once hired, and after their week's annual holiday, the agricultural servants attended their place of work for the coming year. In 1901, Henry Rider Haggard, more famous as a novelist, visited the East Riding as part of a self-imposed enquiry into the state of English agriculture (serialised initially in the **Daily Express**, and then published, in 1902, in two volumes as **Rural England**). His stated aim was to *emulate Arthur Young [1741-1820], who more than a century before, had travelled through and written of the state of agriculture in the majority of the English counties.* Whilst in the county, he visited Eastburn Farm, Driffield, and, amongst other aspects, reported on the hind's cottage:

... We visited the house of the hind, or foreman, with whom Mr. Jordan [the farmer] contracted to board eight or ten of the horsemen, lads and young unmarried men, at a price of about 8s per week per man. The place, which was scrupulously clean, was kept by the hind's wife ... The kitchen, a room of good size, where the men ate and sat, had a large window and fireplace and a floor of well-scrubbed red tiles ... Upstairs, approached by a broad ladder, we saw the large sleeping room, also beautifully neat and clean. It had four beds, two men sleeping in each bed, by which stood boxes with their kits.

Rider Haggard also reported on the farm servants' diet at Eastburn:

At 5.45am, cold beef and bacon, with boiled milk and fruit pie; at midday, beef pie or boiled beef twice a week, and roast beef on Sundays, with potatoes and another vegetable, rice pudding, or fruit pie; at 6.30pm, or 4.45 on Sundays, supper, at which the food was the same as at breakfast. It will be seen that these young men ran no fear of starvation; still often I was told in Yorkshire that they make constant complaints, however well they are fed, and that one of their commonest excuses for leaving a situation is that it is a 'bad meat shop'.

Only when heavy work was in progress and the hours were unusually long, such as at hay-making, during the cereal harvest or when threshing, were additional refreshments, known locally as *lowance* provided, given in mid-morning and mid-afternoon. Generally, this consisted of a sandwich, or some fruit pie or cake, and either tea or beer. Only those actively involved in these tasks were provided with *lowance*. Sometimes, if the number of workers involved were small, the farmer preferred to give a cash supplement rather than refreshments, thus saving disruption to the farmhouse kitchen routine.

14. Harvest *lowance* time at Newby Farm, Huggate, c.1936-38.

8. Living the land

Throughout the nineteenth century and into the first decades of the twentieth, farm workforces were large. For instance, in 1851, the permanent labour force at the combined Eastburn and Eastburn Warren farms, totalling just under 1,300 acres and worked as a single unit, amounted to sixty-seven men and lads, including the two foremen. The census returns for that year give the following breakdown as to the disbursement of the directly employed agricultural workforce: at Eastburn Farm, there were eight unmarried agricultural servants who boarded with the foreman and his family, and thirty-one labourers employed on a daily or, more usually, weekly basis; at Eastburn Warren Farm, there were seven unmarried agricultural servants living with the foreman and his family on the farmstead, and nineteen day- or week-labourers. All the daily and weekly employed workers lived in privately rented properties in the surrounding villages of Kirkburn, Southburn, Garton-on-the-Wolds and Tibthorpe, with a small percentage drawn from the nearby market town of Driffield, and most residing not more than four miles away from their place of employment; a little later, six cottages were built at Eastburn and Eastburn Warren to provide on-site accommodation for part of the married workforce and their families.

In total, therefore, the farms employed sixty-seven agricultural workers. At Eastburn Farm, with its 834 acres, this was equivalent to 20.85 acres per worker, and at Eastburn Warren, with its 466 acres, was equivalent to 17.25 acres per worker. By combining the acreages, an acre:labour ratio of approximately 19:1 is arrived at, comparing very favourably with similar sized holdings in the East Riding at this time.

The wage rates for agricultural servants were discussed in the previous chapter. In 1848, George Legard, in a report to the Royal Agricultural Society of England, recorded the average pay for East Yorkshire agricultural labourers as: from Martinmas to Candlemas, 12s. per week, and from Candlemas to harvest-time, 13s.6d. to 14s. per week. During the harvest period, labourers could earn several shillings more than the highest weekly wage. It is interesting to note that Legard considered the East Riding farm labourers to be among the best-paid in England at this time. By way of comparison, the wage for farm-hands in East Anglia and the southern counties was around 10s. per week.

Farm labourers lived locally, usually in surrounding villages but sometimes in tied cottages situated on, or near, the farms themselves. In the late 1840s, East Riding cottage rents were between £3 and £6 per year, so, using Legard's wage figures as a benchmark, about one-tenth of the labourer's income was spent on accommodation. However, in 1869, some years after the well-designed and well-built farm cottages at Eastburn had been erected, Francis Jordan was charging 1s.3d. per week/£3 per annum as rent, representing just 8.33% of his labourer's weekly wage at that date. This contrasts with the £4 to £8 per year cottage rents which were being charged in the locality at this time, for properties which were, in many instances, in a poor and dilapidated condition.

In addition, there was a fluctuating number of seasonal workers employed at particularly busy times, such as during the cereal and potato harvests. These additional hands were drawn from a wider geographical area and consisted of migrant gangs of men, women and children from the Yorkshire Dales and Ireland, who moved from farm to farm, and were paid by piece-rate.

The gangs traditionally entered the East Riding at the end of July, after working on the hay harvest in the Pennines. They stayed for the cereal harvest, and then, on or about 11 October, moved into Lincolnshire for the potato and sugar beet lifting, before returning home in November or December.

With such large numbers employed on the land, precisely defined hierarchies developed within, and between, the various components of the total workforce. At the pinacle was the foreman, or hind, the lynch-pin between master and men, a powerful figure who, in his domain, ruled supreme. An experienced, influential and steady hand, it was to him that the farmer issued the daily orders, and it was he who was responsible for ensuring that the day's tasks were properly organised and efficiently and proficiently carried out. Beneath the foreman lay the two main cohorts of workers: the agricultural servants - the horselads - and the labourers.

The horselads, each responsible for a team of four or six horses, were the elite element within the farm workforce, and remained so until the advent of mechanisation in the 1940s and 1950s. As a group, the horselads lived and worked within a clearly defined, age-related hierarchical structure. At the top, and oldest, was the waggoner (*wag*), who, although not separated physically or socially, was in a position of authority over all the other lads, ensuring that their work was properly done. Next came the third lad (*thirdy*), followed by the fourth (*fourther*), fifth (*fiver*), etc, depending on the number employed on a particular farm. At the bottom of the hierarchy came the *least lad* - who was the youngest, having just left school and in his first job, and least physically able - who, as his title implies, was last in everything. It was he who had the worst horses in the worst harness, and it was he who was the butt of all jokes. However, as he grew older he would make his way up through the ranks of horselads.

Very few East Riding farms had more than ten lads, and most had far fewer.

With the exception of the Vale of York, there was no second waggoner on East Riding farms: this is explained by the fact that the head waggoner came second, after the foreman, in the hierarchy.

Most farms also had a worker known as *Tommy Owt*, a living-in unmarried lad, whose role was to step into any job when other staff were ill, turning his hand to anything and everything.

Although the hind had responsibility for the horselads and day- and/or weekly-labourers, the farmer himself tended to have direct responsibility for the shepherds and their assistants and for the beastman (*bullocky*) and his assistants, as well as for any grooms employed on the farm.

A mixed farming regime characterised the local agricultural scene throughout the nineteenth and earlier twentieth centuries. This type of farming reached its peak in the era of Victorian prosperity, between the 1840s-70s, and was synonymous with what the Victorians called High Farming . It had, however, taken two or three hundred years for this type of agricultural practice to fully mature. On the medieval farm, livestock was kept and crops were grown, but their production was kept separate and not integrated into a coherent whole; moreover, during the middle ages, production was geared first and foremost to the subsistence requirements of the individual farmer and his family. In the Victorian period, most farms grew crops and reared livestock for sale on the open market, and their production was organised in such a way that each element was dependent on the other for the successful outcome of the entire enterprise. The aim was self-sufficiency, whereby livestock manured the crops, and the crops helped to feed the livestock. The system also ensured that throughout the year there was a surplus of produce to be sold off the farm.

Mixed farming implies the production of at least two commodities. In practice, production on most English farms has always been higher: for example, in East Yorkshire during the 1860s and 1870s a majority of farms produced eight or more commodities and sold at least five off the farm. This diversification had several advantages. Where only one product is sold off, the farmer is at great risk from price fluctuations and the hazards of climate and disease. If livestock commodities, such as eggs, milk and meat are produced, income comes not once a year as it does with crop monoculture, but at regular intervals. Keeping livestock and growing crops also evens out the use of labour across the agricultural year. Crops have seasonal peaks in spring and late summer and early autumn; keeping livestock utilises labour in the slacker months.

Also, growing crops and keeping livestock was mutually beneficial. Part of the arable was used to grow crops to be fed to the animals; temporary grass produced hay and grazing, and the clover in the sward added nitrogen to the soil. Fodder root crops could be fed *in situ* to sheep or lifted and fed to cattle in stalls or yards. The animals provided a liberal supply of dung and farmyard manure, which, when spread on the land, maintained the yield of cereal crops. Cereals, roots and clover were grown in rotation, and this allowed thorough weeding during the year in roots and limited the spread of plant diseases. By-products were utilised: thus, straw could be used as litter in stalls as the basis of farmyard manure and as a feedstuff, while poor quality grain could be fed to the livestock.

Generally speaking, a cropping rotation based on the widely adopted Norfolk system was followed on the Yorkshire Wolds. This was:

Year 1:   Wheat
Year 2:   Turnips
Year 3:   Barley
Year 4:   Clover or rye-grass

As a working sequence this would be: spring corn, undersown with clover or rye-grass, cut for hay or seed and then grazed; wheat, or a crop of rye after the August corn harvest, to be fed off green by livestock in the early spring (at a time when fresh food would be needed for the livestock); then turnips or another root crop, to be fed off the land or carted to cattle.

However, because of the tendency of clover to develop clover sickness on the Wolds, a seven-course rotation was sometimes substituted:

Year 1:   Wheat
Year 2:   Turnips
Year 3:   Barley

Year 4:   Peas
Year 5:   Turnips
Year 6:   Oats
Year 7:   Seeds

There are a number of advantages to the four- or seven-course rotation: it is self-sufficient in that it maintains soil fertility by natural means - animals and crops are completely interdependent; the alternation of deep and shallow root crops makes full use of the soil - different crops use different nutrients; disease and weeds are eliminated over the cycle; labour requirements are fairly well balanced throughout the year; and grain and animal products can be sold throughout the year.

In the lowlands, on the heavy, water-retentive clays, a more diverse range of cropping rotations were to be found. Prior to the eighteenth century, a two-course corn-fallow rotation was common. However, by the early nineteenth century, following enclosure, various rotations were adopted on different soil types: on strong land, a three-course rotation of wheat-beans/oats-fallow was followed; in central Holderness a five-course system of turnips-barley or oats-clover-wheat-peas/beans was followed; and on the warp-lands an elaborate eight-course rotation of oats-oats-rape-wheats/oats-oats-fallow-wheat-beans was commonplace.

November, after the hirings, marked the start of the agricultural year. As autumn gave way to winter, and then spring to summer, work on the farm proceeded apace: breaking up the ground and preparing the seed-bed, sowing, weeding, and harvesting, not to mention threshing, hedging and ditching, lambing, sheep washing and shearing, the daily routine of tending the livestock, and the hundred-and-one other jobs which went to make up the farmworker's year.

The days were long and arduous. In the early twentieth century, a horselad's typical working day in the summer months was:

5.30 am: Out of bed; into stable to feed horses and clean them out; turn horses out into foldyard for a drink; groom them and gear them up ready for work.

6.30 am: Breakfast.

7.00 am: Into stable, where the hind issued the day's orders, followed by fieldwork.

12 midday: Dinner.

1.00 pm: Fieldwork.

5.00 pm: Finish fieldwork; horses returned to stable and turned out into foldyard for a drink; into stable and gear off, followed by feed.

5.30 pm: Tea.

6.00 pm: Horses fed; sponged down, followed by *wisping down* (drying off) and grooming; followed by bedding down with clean straw.

8.00 pm: End of day.

During the winter months, the day started one hour later and finished one hour earlier.

From the mid-nineteenth century onwards, mainly as a result of the Industrial Revolution, mechanisation became an increasing facet of agricultural life in the East Riding, particularly on the extensive Wolds farms with their large fields. Horse-drawn threshing machines were replaced by steam-driven threshers. Steam ploughs and cultivators became common, as did self-acting reapers, which left the cut corn in swathes ready to be bound and stooked. Farmers could acquire the benefits to be had from machinery in several ways: purchasing outright, buying a share in a particular piece of equipment with other farmers and then using it *pro rata*, hiring from landlords, or using the services of contractors. Steadily, as machinery became more generally available, it began to replace labour, a process which has continued right up to the present day.

9. Good times and bad

During the course of the nineteenth century Britain underwent major structural change at all levels - social, economic, political, cultural and institutional. This drive to modernisation, fuelled by massive population expansion, affected all spheres of life, including farming. It was a time during which Britain ceased to be an agrarian and rural-based society and became, instead, an industrial, consumerist and urban-based nation; overall, it was a time when town and country became increasingly separated from each other.

For the first time, farming became a profit-making business, providing produce for sale on the open market. The profit could then be used to pay the farm rent and wages, invest in new ranges of buildings, machinery and other technologies, and provide an income for the farmer and his family. During these decades, farming became inextricably linked with the emerging supply and demand capitalist economy, and, as such, was, like all other industries, exposed to the regular boom-and-bust cycles which characterise this economic formation.

At the beginning of the nineteenth century, in the aftermath of the French Revolutionary and Napoleonic Wars, British agriculture was in acute depression. As grain prices fell more than those of meat, this was most severely felt in arable regions; however, the heavy clay lands were also affected by this downturn, principally because they were more expensive to cultivate than those regions where lighter soils predominated. This was followed in the 1830s by a period of recovery and then remarkable prosperity, which was to last until the late 1870s and early 1880s, and which is generally known as the 'Golden Age of Farming'.

Stimulated by increasing demand and a generally buoyant economy, agricultural prices rose to high levels, generating substantial profits for many farmers, particularly for those in cereal producing areas such as the East Riding. In this area it seems that much of the profit was invested in suites of new farm buildings, in the purchasing of modern machinery and equipment, and, in the lowlands, in extensive land drainage schemes.

Locally, during the 1850s and 1860s, cereals commanded high prices, although these fluctuated from year to year. For instance, in the two decades 1856-1876, wheat sold for between 47s. and 77s. per quarter, with an average price of 57s. per quarter; barley sold for between 28s. and 40s. per quarter, with an average price of 40s. per quarter; and oats sold for between 17s. and 25s. per quarter, with an average price of 21s. per quarter.

At this time, crop yields varied enormously across the East Riding. Available documentary sources for the Wolds record the following figures:

Low Wolds: 28-32 bushels of wheat per acre;
32-40 bushels of barley per acre; and
48-64 bushels of oats per acre.

High Wolds: 42 bushels of wheat per acre;
36 bushels of barley per acre; and
48 bushels of oats per acre.

Similarly, the prices of livestock were high during this period, with, for example, fat ewes fetching between 50s. and 60s. each. Wool, sold to West Yorkshire woollen merchants, was, in the 1860s, sold for between 30s. and 35s. per stone.

Newspaper reports of farm sales give a clear indication of the type and range of machinery and equipment kept on holdings during this time. The following list, taken from an 1872 sale catalogue, is typical of 400-500 acre Wolds farms at the time:

16 horses; 43 cattle; 43 pork and store pigs; 4 superior pole waggons; 1 shaft waggon; 2 broad wheel carts; 2 narrow wheel carts; water cart; Cambridge roller; cylinder roller; single horse wooden roller; 8 rowed corn drill; 2 rowed turnip drill; 3 rowed presser and drill; small turnip drill with roller; iron cultivator; wooden cultivator; iron horse rake; wooden horse rake; swathe rake; hay-making machine; 4 wooden ploughs with wheels and draughts; 1 iron plough with wheels and draughts; 1 iron and 4 wooden scrufflers; 2 chisel-toothed harrows; 1 large wooden harrow; 2 pair of wooden couple harrows; 11 common harrows; chain harrow; 2 dressing machines; 1 Blower patent weigh, 20 stone of weights; straw cutter by Picksley, Sims and Co.; 100 corn bags, hopper and braces; 3 long ladders; 2 short ladders; 2 stack covers; 1 waggon cover; potato washer; 4 wooden pig troughs; small iron pig trough; 6 stand hecks; tumblers; waggon ropes; 6 long and 12 short pig bars; 1 Gardiner's turnip cutter; 2 plough sledges; 2 scalding tubs; 8 hen coops; wheelbarrow; large bacon chest; round bacon chest; barrel churn and frame; 3 leaden bowls and frames; joiner's bench; crosscut saw; hand saw; cake crusher; sundry round tubs; sack barrow; 2 gavelocks; waggon jack; 2 corn bins; gearing for 12 horses; 4 cart saddles; waggon saddle; 2 breechings; 2 waggon pads; 12 pair of waggon traces; 10 pair of plough traces; 6 loose stretchsticks; cart and waggon reins; 3 team chains; riddles; sieves; scuttles; baskets; forks; rakes; scythes; shafts &c. Also a quantity of pitch pine gate spills, several pairs of good oak gate posts, oak and elm planking, 20 good larch poles, 30 pecks of eating potatoes; 1 excellent dog cart, 1 set of harness, ride saddle and bridle.

From the late 1870s onwards, East Yorkshire, along with the rest of England, slid into a severe and prolonged period of agricultural depression. This was to last until the First World War, and saw the fortunes of farming radically reversed, forcing many practitioners into bankruptcy and still more to leave voluntarily. There is much scholarly debate about the causes of this agricultural depression, but the main reasons, varying in their intensity from county to county and from one agricultural regime to another, may be summarised in the following manner:

1. Homegrown cereal and livestock prices fell because of the mass importation of cheaper foreign foodstuffs, chiefly from Argentina, Australia, Canada, New Zealand and the United States of America, aided by improvements in sea-borne transportation, and the introduction of canning and refrigeration.

2. The onset of a period of adverse climatic conditions. Between 1873-82 it was cooler and wetter, and there were exceptionally dry summers in 1884, 1885, 1887, 1892, 1893, 1895 and 1896.

The weather could have dramatic effects on crop yields. For example, the 1879 growing season was cool and wet, and East Yorkshire cereal yields were very low: wheat averaged 14 bushels per acre, barley

19-22 bushels per acre, and oats 40-45 bushels per acre.

3.   Inclement weather dramatically increased the incidence of livestock and crop disease. In particular, the period saw major outbreaks of liver rot in sheep and foot and mouth in cattle, and endemic blight and mildew affected crops. This resulted in lower production and lower profits for farmers, and, as a corollary, increased the quantity of imports.

4.   Exacerbated by high taxation, farm incomes fell and, with them, the wages paid to agricultural workers. Many farmers went out of business, and farms were difficult to let; and many workers left the land and moved into the towns and cities of industrial England.

The effects of this period of depression were especially felt by the Wolds farmers because of the extent to which they relied on both cereals and sheep, the market prices for which slumped badly. Between 1880 and 1914, the price of wheat ranged between 36s. and 22s. per quarter, that of barley between 38s. and 24s. per quarter, and that of oats between 26s. and 16s. per quarter. Within the East Riding, the lowest prices appear to have been obtained in the 1890s and early 1900s.

The price of the wool clip also fell dramatically, helped by cheap imports of the material. A nearly complete set of accounts relating to the sale of wool from Eastburn Farm has survived, allowing the consistently downward trend in prices to be clearly demonstrated:

1872	33s.6d. per stone
1873	20s.0d. per stone
1874	24s.6d. per stone
1875	28s.0d. per stone
1876	20s.0d. per stone

[Figures not available for the nine-year period 1877-1885]

1886	11s.0d. per stone
1887	12s.6d. per stone
1888	11s.6d. per stone
1889	12s.3d. per stone
1890	12s.6d. per stone
1891	11s.6d. per stone
1892	10s.6d. per stone
1893	12s.0d. per stone
1894	12s.0d. per stone
1895	12s.0d. per stone
1896	14s.0d. per stone
1897	11s.0d. per stone
1898	10s.0d. per stone

Overall, the price of wool fell by approximately 50% at Eastburn. This was not an isolated case, but is reflected in all those accounts which have survived from this period.

The fall in both cereal and sheep prices served to undermine mixed farming. Falling wool prices made sheep less and less profitable, and the high labour cost of folding and employing shepherds accelerated their decline. Between the 1880s and the 1930s, there was a dramatic fall in the number of sheep in the lowland counties of eastern England, including East Yorkshire.

As the sheep population fell, so too did the area under root crops; turnips were expensive to hoe, lift and cart to farmyards, as was folding; in contrast, imported feeds such as grains and oil-cakes fell in price and made home-grown feeds of all kinds expensive by comparison. Consequently, the fodder acreage, particularly that of root crops, declined from the 1880s. The turnip in its role as a cleaning crop was replaced by the potato, and, after 1925, by sugar beet. The rise in prominence of sugar beet as a crop within the East Riding during the inter-war years is interesting: official returns show that in 1920, there were just six acres of the crop in the county, by 1925 this had increased to 1,037 acres, by 1930 to 9,194 acres, and by 1940 to 11,240 acres.

Turnips were also fed to cattle. The import of beef from Argentina and elsewhere undercut the prices of all but prime English beef, and so beef production also declined. Cattle and sheep had been kept, in mixed farming, not only for cash sales off the farm, but also to provide plentiful supplies of manure for the cereal crops; indeed, for many farmers in eastern England, this was the prime reason for keeping cattle, which were fed on purchased oil-cake to improve their dung as much as their flesh. The fall in wheat prices from the 1880s, combined with the fall in wool and mutton prices, not only made the folding of sheep uneconomic, but, because wheat was uncompetitive against imports, the cost of producing manure for a cereal with an ever-falling price was becoming prohibitively expensive.

The depressed state of East Riding agriculture is evident from evidence given to the 1893 **Royal Commission on Agricultural Depression**. One extract, from the testimony of Mr. W. Harrison, Secretary of the Malton Agricultural Club and Honorary Secretary of the Yorkshire Union of Agricultural Clubs and Chambers of Agriculture, who farmed 900 acres in the western part of the Riding, will serve to illustrate the local severity of the agricultural downturn:

I take first 150 lambs, and this year they would be 72 lbs. each, and taking it at 9d. per lb., the price 20 years ago, it would amount to £405. At the present time, the same flock would realise £315, or 7d. per lb. Taking the wool from 150 sheep at 9 lbs. per head, and that at 1s.9d. per lb. which was the price 20 years, I make £118.2s.6d., as against £59.1s.3d. to-day. Then the wool from the 100 ewes I put at £61.5s. 20 years ago, and at the present price £30.12s.6d. I estimate that 50 beasts could be kept on the farm [Bossall Farm, Bossall, near Scrayingham], *and out of this herd 12 could be sold annually, and estimating each animal at 50 stones weight, that would be 600 stones of beef, which if sold off at that time at 10s. per stone would have given £300, the price to-day being £210 at 7s. per stone. I will only trouble you with another item and that is wheat. 30 acres of wheat would be grown also, and putting this at 4 quarters per acre, at 60s. per quarter, the price 20 years ago would make £360; and the present price of wheat putting it at 30s. per quarter would make £180. Therefore taking the beef and mutton, the wool and the wheat, 20 years ago they would have produced £1,244.7s.6d.; and in the present year they would produce £794.13s.9d., that shows a difference of £449.13s.9d.*

In 1901, during his tour of East Yorkshire, H. Rider Haggard commented on the depressed state of local agriculture:

At Eastburn, near to Driffield, we were the guests of Mr. Jordan, the well-known breeder of prize Leicester sheep ... I had long conversations with Mr. Hopper, who farmed 1,100 acres of adjoining light land, and was Chairman of the Driffield Pure Cake Company, a very useful co-operative association; with Colonel Staveley, a land owner and farmer; with Mr. H.H. Staveley, his brother, who farmed 1,500 acres, mostly on the Wold; with Mr. Jordan himself, and others.

According to these gentlemen the local rents upon the Wold ran from 10s. to 18s., and upon the lower lands from 18s. to 25s. per acre, the fall from the good times averaging about 30 per cent. Two of them at least told us that were it not that they had good homes, where their fathers had lived before them, and considerate landlords they would give up farming, which was becoming a worse business every year. One said that he had actually lost a considerable sum of money, and another that if it had not been for private means at his back he could not have gone on. They thought that were it not for such private means many farmers would be in the Bankruptcy Court who at present were existing, not upon the fruits of their industry, but on money accumulated by themselves or their fathers in the past when farming paid. Others were just making a living; while the only people who did any good were those who had some speciality, such as the breeding of hackneys. They seemed to see no opening in the clouds, and all of them held that foreign competition was actually on the increase and likely to become still more severe.

There were still applications for farms, but they thought the class of tenant was very different from what it had been, and that the sons of the men of the old stamp were not going into farming; one of them backing his opinion with the remark that he had two sons, but it would be very much against his will if either of them took up that profession. As an instance of the dreadful fall in prices Mr. Jordan produced his books and showed us how in the year 1872 his wool sold for £1,608, while in 1900 practically the same weight of clip produced but £333 ... They considered 1901 to be one of the worst seasons ever experienced, at any rate for farmers of the lighter land.

Of labour they said that the old men who had been with their fathers and themselves for many many years were excellent, but that generally it was bad, and getting even scarcer, as the young fellows nearly all went away. This was confirmed by Dr. Brand, a medical officer for the Driffield Union, who told me that the young folk were all deserting the parishes, of which the population was sinking, as the demand for healthy countrymen in the towns was eager and continuous ...

The only bright spot they could see in the local farming outlook was that the dry pastures in other counties could not support sheep in 1901, which were consequently cheap to buy, and ought to fat out at a profit on their wold turnips. Many fields, however, were almost bare of roots that season. Colonel Staveley was of opinion that better cottages were wanted and would be of some help, and all agreed that it would be well if money could be borrowed from the Government on easier terms to be used in building such cottages. They thought also that boys in the rural schools should be let out on the land in summer and kept to their books in winter. They seemed to be of opinion moreover ... that there should be some alteration or strengthening of the law with reference to the sale of foreign meat, so as to make it impossible for dishonest butchers to palm off such meat upon customers as English-grown.

At this time agricultural wages for horsemen were between £24 and £26 per annum, and those of lads were around £16. Farm labourers were paid 17s.6d. per week.

The onset of the First World War marked a substantial change in the fortunes of the farming community, change which was driven by an increasing demand for agricultural produce and the resulting high prices; concomitantly, this period saw an all too brief return to agricultural prosperity. The period also marks the beginnings of state intervention in, and subsidies for, British farming.

As the effects of the conflict tightened, Britain's imported foodstuffs became increasingly vulnerable to German naval attacks; once again, the country had to become agriculturally self-sufficient, not only in terms of feeding the civilian population but also in supplying the armies on the Western Front and elsewhere.

Perhaps the most significant agricultural instrument of these years was the 1917 Corn Production Act. This piece of legislation had a number of purposes: it guaranteed the price of wheat and oats until 1922; introduced minimum wages for farmworkers; limited rent increases for tenancies; introduced powers to control cultivation in the national interest ; significantly extended the the area under arable cultivation; and appointed County Agricultural Executive Committees to oversee the extension of arable cultivation. Maximising output was the unequivocal aim.

At the same time, state interventionist policies were pursued to control prices in order to reduce their impact on the population in general. These covered cereals, potatoes, meat, cheese, milk, and butter.

The following statistics, as detailed in the surviving accounts and valuations from a number of northern Wolds farms, serve to illustrate the rapid upward movement in cereal prices between 1914 and 1919:

1914: Wheat @ 28s. per quarter; barley @ 31s. per quarter; and oats @ 20s. per quarter.

1915: Wheat @ 50s. per quarter; barley @ 35s. per quarter; and oats @ 21s. per quarter.

1916: Wheat @ 60s. per quarter; barley @ 53s. per quarter; and oats @ 32s. per quarter.

1917: Wheat @ 80s. per quarter; barley @ 74s. per quarter; and oats @ 50s. per quarter.

1918: Wheat @ 74s. per quarter; barley @ 68s. per quarter; and oats @ 45s. per quarter.

1919: Wheat @ 75s. per quarter; barley @ 68s. per quater; and oats @ 50s. per quarter.

During the course of the war, the acreage under arable cultivation expanded dramatically across the entire country. On the eve of the First World War there were 10.28 million acres under tillage in Britain; by 1918 this had risen to 12.36 million acres. This increase was undertaken through the offices of the County Agricultural Executive Committees, bodies composed of landowners, farmers and others, who were charged with the implementation of the government's war-time farming policy at the local level. The increase in acreage was achieved through the ploughing up of grasslands and the under-drainage of marginal areas, and the Committees had the power to take in hand those farms where the owner was not prepared to co-operate in the plough policy .

As part of the plough policy and because large numbers of working horses were requisitioned by the military and because of manpower shortages, agricultural mechanisation received an important boost during the war years, but more particularly after the passing of the Corn Production Act. Although tractors first made their appearance in 1902, this period saw the large-scale application of the machine for the first time. Between 1917 and 1919 twenty-six types of tractor made their appearance in British fields, including the Avery (28 HP, USA-made, costing £500), Clayton and Shuttleworth caterpillar (35 HP, British-made, costing £650), Bates Steel Mule (30 HP, British-made, costing £485), Fordson (22 HP, USA-made, costing £280), Mogul (30 HP, USA-made, costing £580), Titan (25 HP, USA-made, costing £410), Overtime (28 HP, USA-made, costing £368), and Universal (25 HP, British-made, costing £510).

The tractors, along with other equipment such as ploughs, harrows, binders and threshing sets, were ordered from manufacturers by the government via its Ministry of Munitions (Agricultural Machinery Branch). Apart from the small number of existing tractors in private ownership, these new machines were owned by the government and their supply to individual localities was orchestrated through the Food Production Department of the Board of Agriculture and the County War Agricultural Committees. By 1918, some 9,000 tractors had been ordered at a cost of £2.13 million. Existing tractors in private ownership - about 3,500 - were temporarily taken over by the County Committees, either by hiring, borrowing or, in some cases, buying them outright.

The extension of arable areas, plus the increased usage of a range of fertilisers (sodium nitrate, ammonium sulphate, superphosphate, and basic slag), saw crop yields, although heavily dependent on climatic factors, steadily increase throughout the war. For example, take the case of wheat: in 1914 the British yield was 1,706,000 tons, 1,961,000 tons in 1915, 1,559,000 tons in 1916, 1,634,000 tons in 1917, and 2,428,000 tons in 1918.

In the later stages of the First World War local agricultural wages were high. Foremen were earning from £60 upwards, waggoners between £50 and £60, lads between £35 and £45, and boys between £20 and £22 per year.

With a return to free trade, the inter-war years saw a return to agricultural depression, severely exacerbated by the 1929-39 international crisis. This period of downturn primarily affected arable districts, such as East Yorkshire.

The decline in cereal prices in the county can be tracked from the following statistics. In 1920-21 cereal prices held, with wheat selling for between 80s. and 76s.6d. per quarter, barley for between 120s. and 70s. per quarter, and oats for between 63s. and 40s. per quarter. With the removal of the price guarantees in the latter year, prices steadily declined, as the snapshots below indicate:

1923: Wheat @ 44s. per quarter; Barley @ 40s. per quarter; and Oats @ 28s. per quarter.

1927: Wheat @ 41s.6d. per quarter; Barley @ 44s. per quarter; and Oats @ 26s. per quarter.

1931: Wheat @ 23s.6d. per quarter; Barley @ 34s. per quarter; and @ Oats 21s. per quarter.

1935: Wheat @ 20s. per quarter; Barley @ 28s. per quarter; and Oats @ 19s. per quarter.

1939: Wheat @ 18s.6d. per quarter; Barley @ 21s. per quarter; and Oats @ 17s. per quarter.

The 1920s saw the direct subsidisation of food production by the state, the introduction of tariffs and quotas on imported foodstuffs, and reorganisation schemes, principally in the marketing of agricultural produce, aimed at promoting efficiency and modernisation - for example, the establishment of the Milk Marketing Board. In 1932, a Wheat Act was passed by parliament, which guaranteed a standard price of 10s. per hundredweight; if the market price fell below the standard, farmers would have their income made up to that level.

During the 1930s many farmers were forced out of business. The bankruptcy sales notices - and there were many - which appeared in local newspapers give a good indication of the range of implements and livestock maintained on farms at this time. The following example, taken from a mid-1930s issue of the **Driffield Times**, relating to a 450-acre Wolds farm, is typical:

20 horses; 87 cattle; 444 sheep; 5 waggons; 2 rullies; 6 carts; 2 corn drills; turnip drill; 2 Massey Harris 6ft. binders; water cart; 4-sheave press drill; 6 Ransome ploughs; Hall plough; J.H.B. plough; 3 sets swing chisel harrows; 4 sets gib harrows; 2 sets spring-tined iron harrows; 2 sets gate harrows; set big harrows; Martin cultivator; 6 scrufflers; spring-tined harrow; 2 horse rakes; numerous baulks, draughts and tools; weigh and weights; 2 sack barrows; sack elevator; sack bin; quantity of bags; 2 cake crushers; 3 turnip cutters; quantity of tumbrils and pig troughs; large hen hut, coops etc.; 6 ladders; International tractor; 3-furrow Ransome plough; 6-furrowed riffler; Massey Harris cultivator; Ransome cultivator; Clayton and Shuttleworth threshing machine and elevator; International transport 6 h.p. Amanco engine; Bamford mill; 7ft. McCormick power binder; shepherd's hut; 25 troughs; 30 wire nets and stakes; 100 new bars, digs, turnip tools, etc.; gearing complete for 14 horses; 4 cart saddles; 3 sets of waggon breechings; 3 pads; wood joiner's shop; contents of joiner's shop; contents of blacksmith's shop; duck house; 400 gall. paraffin tank.

The period c.1926-39 saw a reduction in the number of working horses on East Riding farms, from approximately 24,000 to 17,000. Although mechanisation was slowly proceeding, this factor does not account for the decline. Rather, as tractors only replaced three or four horses each, it seems that the main reason for their decline was as a result of the depression and a consequential reduction in the farmers' power requirements; at Eastburn Farm, for instance, between November 1930 and March 1931 eighteen out of a total of thirty-six horses were sold off.

Similarly, wage rates were depressed during the inter-war years. In the late 1920s and early 1930s, farm foremen were earning between £45 and £50, waggoners between £25 and £30, and lads from £14 to £20 per year.

As with the First World War, the Second War revived the fortunes of agriculture. As the storm clouds gathered over Europe during the spring and summer of 1939, preparations were made to place Britain's agricultural production on a war footing. By September 1939, the County War Agricultural Executive Committees had been established once again, and the Women's Land Army was also in place. Whilst the Ministry of Agriculture took farming into direct control, the Ministry of Food became responsible for overseeing the marketing and distribution of foodstuffs.

The Ministry of Agriculture also fostered, through the agency of the County War Agricultural Executive Committees, the formation of local farmers' discussion groups. These proved valuable for the dissemination of government policy as well as useful forums for the exchange of information and ideas between farmers and other agriculturalists. Locally, a number of these discussion groups are still active, in the Brandesburton, Burton Agnes, Burton Fleming and Fimber areas. In general, the development of agricultural education in the East Riding, of which these groups are a part, is a subject that would repay detailed study.

With the threat of German U-boats and surface attack vessels, self-sufficiency once again became a necessity, and farmers, with some urging from the government, began ploughing up grassland, on which wheat, in particular, was grown. In the first year of the war, over 1 million acres of additional land was brought into arable cultivation. With the enhanced fertility locked into grasslands which had not been ploughed since the end of the First World War, crop yields rose dramatically throughout the 1939-40 period. Despite high yields, and with rationing in place, food prices also increased, as the following local examples illustrate:

1939: Wheat @ £4.3s.3d. per ton (this was the first time that wheat grown in the East Riding had sold for less than £5 per ton since the 1850s-60s); barley @ £5.5s. per ton.

1940: Wheat @ £10 per ton; barley @ £12 per ton.

1941: Wheat @ £13 per ton; barley @ £19 per ton.

1942: Wheat @ £15 per ton; barley @ £28 per ton.

1943: Wheat @ £22 per ton; barley @ £35 per ton.

1944: Wheat @ £30 per ton; barley @ £26 per ton.

1945: Wheat @ £12 per ton; barley @ £22 per ton.

One of the most interesting events affecting local agriculture during the Second World War occured in May 1943, when large parts of the Wolds were requisitioned by the military authorities as tank and battlefield training areas in the months leading up to D-Day. This, taking place at the height of the Battle of the Atlantic and when Britain was suffering severe food shortages, resulted in about 210,000 acres of land being taken out of full-time production for a period of ten months or so. Whilst arable activities continued on a much reduced scale, the entire sheep population had to be sold off. In the early summer of 1943 some 100,000 sheep were disposed of at specially convened markets across the region. For example, at Weaverthorpe, between 18-20 May, the flocks of 74 farms, amounting to 13,613 animals, were disposed of. And this was a scene repeated all over the affected area. Of course, the farmers were compensated for their loss, but this event marked the end of the dominance of wool-producing flocks on the Wolds, which, in turn, reduced the acreages under turnips, and then, subsequently, gave rise to widespread potato growing. The sheep sales also marked the beginning of the end of the mixed farming regime which had dominated the Yorkshire Wolds for the previous one hundred and fifty years. Despite the dislocation, and the damage caused by military manoeuvres, arable production fell by only an estimated 40%. By March 1944 this episode had come to an end, with the troops and their equipment relocated to the south of England to commence the build-up for the invasion of Europe.

In 1940, national minimum wage rates for agricultural workers were introduced at 48s. per week for adult males. This was raised to 60s. per week in December 1941, to 65s. in December 1943, and to 75s. in March 1945.

Overall, the challenges thrown out by the war, and the way in which the farming community quickly responded to the increased requirements of the nation's food supply, demonstrated that the agricultural sector was both adaptable and basically healthy, despite years of recession.

The Second World War increased the scale of mechanisation on British farms: nationally, in 1939, there were 56,200 tractors in use, by 1945 this had risen to just over 200,000; and this increase is reflected across a whole range of farm implements, from balers to milking machines. Thereafter, the pace quickened. By the late 1940s, the range of equipment on East Riding farms showed an increasing trend towards mechanisation, as the list from a 600-acre Wolds farm sale catalogue of 1948 serves to demonstrate:

3 horses; Case D.C. 4 Rowcrop tractor; Case Model D tractor on rubbers with spade lugs for rear wheels; Case Model C tractor on rubbers; all-steel Marshall 54ins. threshing machine with barrel self-feeder; elevator with turn-table; 7 rubber-tyred tractor trailers; 2 rullies; 2 rubber-tyred carts; 2 heavy carts on irons; water cart; 2 8ft. power-drive Massey Harris binders; tractor hay sweep; horse hay sweep; Bambford Progress hay-maker; grass mower; circular blade hedge slasher; Knapp Monarch power-lift; 17-coultered force-feed corn drill; Yates small seeds drill; Knapp 4-rowed turnip drill; 2 sheaf-press drills; bean drill; 2 Albion Endless Chain manure drills; tractor gang rollers; Cambridge roller; flat roller; 11-tined Nicholson drag; 11-tined Ransome Dauntless drag; shim; tool bar scruffler for Case D.C. 4 tractor; 2 sets of Massey Harris spring harrows; pitch pole harrow; Massey Harris disc harrow; 2 sets of tractor chisel harrows; 3-horse chisel harrow; 2 sets of spring-tine harrows; set of 4 light seed harrows; set of 3 diamond spring-tine harrows; set of wooden small seed harrows; set of 2 wick harrows; 4 wood harrows; Kent turnip gapper; 4 single scrufflers; 2-rowed scruffler; 4-rowed turnip harrow; 3 iron single ploughs; 3 digger ploughs; 2 Ransome R.S.L.M. 3-furrow tractor ploughs; 6-furrow Ransome riffler plough.

In the early post-war years, the East Riding gave up its working horses relatively quickly. By 1950 there were only about 6,000 horses and at the end of the decade this figure had dropped to less than 2,000, and their breeding had virtually ceased. As a method of cultivation, the tractor was cheaper than the horse team. The age of the working farm horse was over. The demise of the horse also brought in its wake reductions in farm labour forces. In the mid-nineteenth century, a local 600-acre farm would have required a workforce of 30-40 men, by the late 1950s this would have dropped to 12-15, which, with the increasing scale and power of machinery and further periods of agricultural depression, would have been reduced to one or two men by the 1990s. Nationally, in 1949 there were 648,200 workers in agriculture, by 1965 this had dropped to 385,900, by 1980 to 255,100, and by 1998 to 133,100.

As the twentieth century progressed, farm workers became paid weekly according to national scales, which were set by the Agricultural Wages Board. By the mid-1960s, adult male workers (over 20 years of age) in the industry were receiving 210s. for a 44-hour working week, with an overtime rate set at 7s.2d. per hour. Those male workers aged 15-19 years received between 96s.6d. and 178s.6d. per week, with overtime payments of between 3s.3d. and 6s.1d. per hour. Adult female workers (over 20 years of age) were receiving 157s.6d. for the same working week, with overtime payments set at 5s.4d. per hour. Those female workers aged between 15-19 years received between 86s. and 153s.6d. per week, with overtime rates of between 2s.11d. and 5s.3d. per hour.

By the end of the twentieth century, standard agricultural workers (male and female over 19 years of age) were earning a minimum national rate of £170.23 for a 39-hour working week, with overtime payments of £6.55 per hour, and enhanced payments for additional responsibilities and qualifications. Those male and female workers aged 15-18 years were receiving between £85.12 and £144.70 for the same working week, with overtime payments ranging between £3.27 and £5.57 per hour.

Since 1945 farming has changed beyond recognition, leading some commentators to describe the pace and scale of developments as constituting a second agricultural revolution.

As well as mechanisation, the pivotal theme dominating the agricultural scene since 1945 has been the issue of subsidies, which, arguably, have been responsible for the recurrent crises suffered by the industry over the last fifty years. The 1947 Agriculture Act was central to the genesis of subsidies. By providing the agricultural sector with a substantial degree of price security, the post-war Atlee government hoped, at a time when food rationing was still in place, to encourage the expansion of farming and give it a central role in the country's economic reconstruction.

For the first time, comprehensive production subsidies were introduced on all major farm products. Henceforth, irrespective of world market prices, farmers were to receive guaranteed prices for what they grew and reared. In the process, farming became a factory production line, the price of land became inflated, and farmers, aided by a whole array of new crop strains and artificially manufactured fertilisers and pesticides, were encouraged to over-produce. The introduction of subsidies also resulted in the end of mixed farming; price guarantees meant that there was no need to maintain a range of activities as insurance against the variability of the weather and fluctuating market demands. Also, with the advent of agri-chemicals the requirement of maintaining a fixed crop rotation largely became a thing of the past; it was now possible, for instance, to grow three, four or five cereal crops in succession without all the problems which would have occured previously under the organic system of farming.

Britain's membership of the European Economic Community (EEC) in 1973 reinforced still further the principle of price support for farmers, and, in the process, turned the agricultural industry into a contentious subject. External borders were closed to imports, thereby protecting farmers from overseas competition, the price of home-produced foodstuffs was artificially inflated by the removal of supplies from the market and the intervention purchasing system was introduced (annually set target prices were established and if prices fell below this to an intervention price - a tenth or so below the target price - then the government bought from farmers at that price). Commodity prices escalated and farmers, within the framework of the Common Agricultural Policy, were encouraged to still higher levels of production. The era of the grain, beef and butter mountains had dawned, indicating that agricultural output had outrun demand. For comparison, British agricultural output in the early 1980s was two-and-a-half times that of the 1930s, four times that of the 1870s, and nine times that of the early decades of the nineteenth century. Whilst it is also true that population levels expanded dramatically during this period, production has, even so, outstripped demand, particularly over the last fifty years.

During the 1980s a consensus emerged amongst politicians and others that the entire question of subsidies needed to be addressed and that modifications designed to slowdown output had to be made. It was in this context that quotas were introduced, first on milk, later extended to sheep and cattle, and then as set-aside on land.

After the prosperous 1970s and 1980s English agriculture began to slide once more into recession, with the late 1990s developing into the worst period of depression since the 1930s, thus reflecting the cyclical boom and bust nature of the capitalist market system in general. The BSE crisis, the strong £ sterling, the collapse of the Russian markets and the mass importation of cheap foodstuffs have all played their part in precipitating the present situation. Whilst all sectors of agriculture have been affected, some have suffered more adversely than others, in particular the livestock producers and small owner-occupiers, who have seen their livelihood dissipate before their eyes.

Striking parallels are beginning to emerge between the 1930s depression and the present one: farmers are focusing more on diversification, on co-operation (the sharing of equipment, for instance), there is a mounting exodus of practitioners from the industry, and there is much talk about a return to an organic system of farming. One major difference is that now there are very few jobs to be shed; mechanisation has reduced employment on the land to such an extent that it is difficult to see how the relatively few workers left in the industry could be reduced further.

What of the future? That farming will survive the present crisis is not in question, but just what its character will be in ten or fifteen years time is difficult to predict. Lessons from the past, however, do indicate that the industry has the ability to withstand long periods of depression, that it is adaptable, and that it can successfully confront the many challenges that it has been faced with over the last two hundred years.

10. The Driffield Agricultural Society

One of the effects of the Agricultural Revolution was to generate great interest in scientific methods of farming amongst practitioners, as well as more widely. Many books and newspaper and journal articles were produced during the later eighteenth century and throughout the nineteenth, aimed at disseminating the latest thinking, and drawing attention to new developments, equipment and methods, as well as presenting the results of various agricultural experiments.

In consequence of this thirst for knowledge and improvement, and stimulated by the agricultural sector emerging from a period of depression, many local, county and national agricultural societies and clubs and institutions came into being during the middle decades of the nineteenth century - for example: the Yorkshire Agricultural Society, founded in 1837; the English Agricultural Society, formed in 1838 (renaming itself the Royal Agricultural Society of England in 1840 after receiving a Royal Charter); the Rothamsted Experimental Station was established in 1843; and two years later the Agricultural College at Cirencester came into existence. All of these bodies - and many more - had, as their principle aims, the promotion of good farming in general, the fostering of invention and research, and the stimulation of progress in all branches of agriculture.

Within this broad sequence of developments, a Farmers' Club was in existence at Driffield by at least 1851. Unfortunately, the origins, membership and activities of this group are largely unknown, although, in 1852, they did hold experiments with new agricultural machinery on Kelleythorpe Farm. In 1853, the Farmers' Club reconstituted itself as the Driffield and East Riding Agricultural Society. As well as organising meetings to discuss and promote good practice, the Society had, from the beginning, the intention of organising an annual Agricultural Show in the town. The 1853 show never happened because of an apparent lack of interest. However, in the following year the first annual one-day Driffield Show was held, instituting a tradition which, with a few exceptions, has continued right up to the present. An informative contemporary description of the first show, presided over by Mr. E.H. Reynard, the Society's first president, was printed in **The Farmer's Magazine**, and is worth quoting:

The Driffield Agricultural Society held its first annual exhibition of farm stock, poultry, horses, and implements in a field within a short distance of the town, on Wednesday, the 12th of July, where it was clearly demonstrated that union is the strength of the farmer when spiritedly put into action, without looking for, or feeling that the great and rich are indispensable to the existence of agricultural societies, however advantageous their pecuniary aid and patronage may be to all societies whose object is the furtherance of improvement and social progress.

The success of all societies depends upon the committee and secretary who manage the affairs thereof; also much of the success attending this day's exhibition lay in the selection of gentlemen well-known as first-rate judges of the animals on which they were called to adjudicate, and appointing three judges for each description of stock. This might have been carried also to the appointing two sets for the horses, as it frequently happens that parties who are first-rate judges of cart or farm-horses are not good judges of riding horses, hunters, &c., and vice versa. This society also observed another good plan, namely, having their judges gentlemen from some considerable distance - preventing that unfortunate petty feeling that disappointed aspirants so generally whisper about the favouritism shown to this one and the other. From the duties of the judges being concentrated on only one sort of stock, there was plenty of time to scrutinize and calculate with greater certainty the comparative merits of each animal; therefore the awards were almost universally placed right, giving most general satisfaction, although in many cases the merits in animals were so closely balanced, that many good judges could not satisfy themselves to which the palm ought to be given; yet, after the three judges had agreed upon the award, all seemed to feel satisfied.

The quantity and quality of cattle, sheep, pigs, poultry, horses, and implements exhibited, far surpassed the most sanguine expectations of the spirited originators of this society, and the large assembly of noblemen, clergy, gentlemen, farmers, and labourers who visited the show. They were admitted by tickets, at two-and-sixpence, from 10 o'clock until 12, when shilling tickets were issued. The society sold nearly three hundred pounds' worth of tickets, and we have since learned that labourers were admitted at about three o'clock at threepence each. The number of tickets sold, we ascertained, reached about six thousand, which proves the show was appreciated by the wisdom-seeking sons and daughters of the East Riding. It is truly gratifying to see the orderly, cool, close inspection the young, as well as the old, gave to each class, and to hear the many wise maxims and quaint observations that were passed from sire to son; also the spirit with which the ladies entered into the merits and demerits of the stock in general, especially the poultry, of which there was a capital show. The universal interest and spirit displayed,

proved the vast advantages that were accruing from the society's efforts, and augurs well for its future prosperity ...

In total, there were 720 entries to the various classes, and £282.17s.6d. was awarded in prize monies.

The above report marks the beginning of a more or less continuous, and comprehensive, coverage of the activities of the Society in both the specialised farming press and its more popular counterparts. In the absence of any surviving minute books for the period prior to the 1930s, these reports are important sources of evidence for the Society's activities.

The first year's Show proved a success, and reports of the second event clearly demonstrate that it was more ambitious, having expanded to include a number of additional exhibitions and demonstrations designed to foster innovation and experimentation amongst the farming community. As **The Farmer's Magazine** correspondent wrote:

The second annual show of this flourishing and important society was held at Driffield, on Wednesday, July 11 ... in a field near the King's Mill ... Nearly £400 were offered in premiums [prizes], and there were upwards of 900 entries. Many special premiums were offered by private individuals for certain descriptions of stock. The show ... presented a splendid array of shorthorns, sheep, horses, pigs and poultry. There was also a very large display of machinery and implements, the object of the committee being particularly directed to the encouragement of implements combining novelty of invention and practical utility; and for the promotion of this object a very handsome sum was set apart in premiums. A new and pleasing feature at this show was the exhibition of specimens of approved manure; for we think the produce of abundant crops is of equal importance to the agriculturalist as the rearing and feeding of superior stock. Amongst these were samples of ammonia-phosphate, for wheat, oats, barley, and grass; and nitro-phosphate, for turnips, rape, and other bulbous-root crops, manufactured by Hodgson and Simpson, Wakefield, and Matthews and Co., manufacturing agricultural chemists, Driffield. These manures were stated to stand peculiarly high in the estimation of the public, having stood the test of eight years' experience by most of the leading farmers in Yorkshire and Lincolnshire. The nitro-phosphate has been proved to be the best substitute for guano as a manure for turnips, being the most rich in the elements which give so much value to that celebrated manure. It is also valuable from its highly-concentrated state, and, by means of a drill invented by Mr. Matthews, can be drilled by itself, without any mixture of ashes or riddled soil, at the rate of from two to two and a half cwt. per acre, which is sufficient to produce and excellent crop of turnips, and the seed is not in the least injured, thus effecting a saving in the expense of carting, mixing, and manual labour of from 4s. to 6s. per acre: this economic drill obtained a prize.

The 1854 and 1855 shows set the format for succeeding years. That the annual event quickly became established, and of some significance in the county agricultural calendar, is demonstrated by an account of the 30 July 1856 show, which appeared in **The Farmer's Magazine**:

During the last week the East Riding of Yorkshire has been in a state of exhilarating commotion, by the repetition of a series of agricultural exhibitions, any one of which would do credit to the industrial enterprise and skill of any county in England. The first was at Bridlington, and was pronounced to be one of the most successful held there for the long period of twenty years. The second was at Market Weighton, including the districts of Selby and Tadcaster, and excited general surprise by the greatness of the quantity and the excellence of the quality of the stock shown. The third was at Driffield on Friday, and for the immense number of people present, and superiority and extent of the stock, and the spirited manner in which the proceedings were conducted, completely eclipsed the two neighbouring shows. Much of the good feeling which prevails in the East Riding may be attributed to the frequency of these agricultural exhibitions, which serve to keep the agricultural mind in a state of competitive activity; and nothing can more strongly attest the growing prosperity of agriculture in England than the annual increase of these really splendid exhibitions.

The show at Driffield was all that could be wished: the weather was glorious, and the attendance very numerous. Seven thousand people were admitted to the ground, and nearly £300 was taken at the gate for admission. Nearly £400 was given in prizes. The show of shorthorns and yearling bulls was particularly noticeable as being exceedingly fine. Of sheep and horses a finer set never came together; and the judges had great difficulty in coming to a decision as to the merits of the different rams. There were nearly 400 horses on the ground, of the finest description: hunters were particularly good. There was also a good show of pigs. Poultry was a magnificent show, there being no less than 260 pens, including 23 game cocks. Implements were very numerous, of which there were 50 stands.

In consequence of the great success which has attended the application of artificial manures in the district, the samples exhibited excited a good deal of interest and discussion on the ground.

After the show a dinner took place in the Corn Exchange, which was handsomely decorated for the occasion with trophies and banners. Upwards of 200 gentlemen sat down to dinner. Lord Londesborough, the President of the Society, presided ... Lord Londesborough's band was in attendance ...

From the late 1850s onwards, the exhibition of machinery became of ever increasing importance on show day, reflecting both the trend towards farm mechanisation and the general prosperity of agriculture at the time. The presence of national, as well as more local, implement and machinery manufacturers became a characteristic feature of the show, on whose stands the latest designs, technologies and developments could be demonstrated to prospective purchasers -the age of the agricultural salesman had arrived!

After about 1860, the Driffield Show appears to change direction somewhat. Rather than being just an annual agricultural exhibition, it became integrated into the wider cultural life of the town; the show was now a town event, a day to be enjoyed by the whole community. Indeed, from quite early on, farmworkers in the district were given Show day off work, and this perquisite became an implicit part of their contracts of employment.

The 1861 Show, on Saturday 27 July, was held on two fields off Shady Lane (now Victoria Road), and attendance was between 7,000 and 8,000 people. In addition, the town was decorated with bunting, there were stalls in the Market Place, fairground attractions on Cross Hill, and photographers in the streets. In the evening musical

15. Bronze medal issued to Driffield Show prize winners during the nineteenth century. On the obverse, around the edge, is the inscription *The Driffield and East Riding Agricultural Society Established 1854*, whilst the centre contains farming scenes, various implements and livestock breeds.

entertainment was provided on the show field by the Driffield Rifle Corps Band, the Nafferton Saxhorn Band and the Barnsley Bell Ringers, followed by a Ball. A dinner was also held at the Corn

Exchange for judges, officials, subscribers, and invited guests. This set the format for many successive Shows.

In 1867 there was a change of venue and day. The Show was held on Friday 27 July, and this day remained Show Day until relatively recently. The venue consisted of four fields off Beverley Lane (now St. John's Road).

No Show was held in 1869 because of a serious outbreak of Foot and Mouth disease. Thereafter, annual events were held until 1874. In 1875 no Driffield Show was held because the three-day Yorkshire Show of the Yorkshire Agricultural Society took place at nearby Elmswell.

From the outset, the intention of the Society was to hold meetings as well as organise the annual show. However, as the years progressed, the organisation of the show became more and more important, and, accordingly, other activities suffered. By the 1880s there was a general concern amongst the local farming community that the Society was neglecting its wider aims. This concern found expression when a meeting was convened at the Cross Keys Hotel, Driffield, in September 1884. The stated purpose of this meeting, under the chairmanship of Mr. James Hopper of Kelleythorpe Farm, was to discuss the formation of a Society to *place the farming industry of the district on a more scientific basis and to teach the newest developments of agriculture by means of lectures and discussions*. This was agreed; a committee consisting of some of the leading farmers in the area was established, a programme of lectures was arranged, and a subscription of 10s. per year was set. In effect, this was the relaunching of the Driffield Farmers' Club, the predecessor of the Driffield and East Riding Agricultural Society.

The club survived until 1899, providing members with regular meetings and discussions on the latest developments in farming. Unfortunately, no archive material appears to have survived from which its activities can be reconstructed. Its demise was probably related to the severe agricultural depression and its disheartening effect on farmers.

16. Turnstile entrance to the 1906 Driffield Show on St. John's Road.

17. Poster advertising the 1907 Driffield Show.

18. A 1913 Driffield Show first prize winner. This well turned-out horse and dog-cart belonged to the Porritt family, village carriers at East and West Lutton.

With few exceptions, a Show was held annually until 1913, at various locations around the town: behind the Board School, Wansford Road; St. John's Road; and Bridlington Road. However, since before the turn of the century, the Society had been struggling to survive: membership was down, attendance at the Show was down, and financial reserves were being depleted. During the late 1890s and early 1900s, attendance at the Show was averaging 1,500 people per event. Gate money did not always cover costs. In 1913, after loosing £18 on that year's Show, the Society was £5.16s.11d. in deficit, and, at a special meeting on 15 April 1914, the decision was taken to wind up the Society. Most of the Society's troubles during these years were a reflection of the severe agricultural recession.

However, between fifty and sixty guarantors came forward and the decision was rescinded. A Show was held in 1914, and a small profit was made on the event. It was at this time also that the name of the Society was changed from the Driffield and East Riding Agricultural Society to the Driffield Agricultural Society. Three weeks after the 1914 Show, the First World War began, and no further Shows were held until 1920.

Annual Shows were held between 1920 and 1930, and, as a consequence of the inter-war depression, the Society steadily lost money on the event. Ironically, as the Society made consistent losses year on year, attendance at the Show steadily increased, with gates of 6,000 to 7,000 people throughout the 1920s. Because of the adverse financial position, with £140 owing to the bank at the end of 1930, no Shows were held between 1931 and 1936.

In early 1937, amid much controversy, a groundswell of opinion developed amongst the membership that a Show should be held that year, a move which was rejected by the then Committee. The decision to hold the Show was carried and the Society's elected officials resigned in protest. Mr. Peter Atkinson was appointed Secretary and an entirely new Committee was established, with Sir Richard Sykes as President. The change of personnel had the effect of reviving what had become a moribund organisation, laying firm foundations for future developments, and setting the Society on a course which would ultimately lead to the thriving organisation of the present.

In 1937 a successful half-day Show was organised, with evening entertainments on the Recreation Ground. The same format was followed in 1938 and 1939, when attendances reached nearly 4,000 and a profit of £101 was made. With the outbreak of the Second World War the Society's activities were suspended for the duration of the conflict.

With the resumption of peace, a Show was held in 1946 and then annually up to the present time. Throughout the late 1940s and early 1950s the event continued to expand, particularly in relation to trade stands, and to make a profit; by 1952 the bank balance stood at £883. Within this context, and following a highly successful 1952 Show, a decision was made by the Society to purchase its own permanent showground at Kelleythorpe, on the western outskirts of the town. Development of the 51-acre site began immediately: the ground was levelled, drained and put down to grass, a belt of trees was planted around the perimeter, three entrances were made, and areas designated for car parking; the actual showground extended over 16 acres, the remainder being given over to car parking facilities. The new showground was opened by Lord Halifax on 29 July 1953, marking a new phase in the Society's history. Attendance that year topped 8,000, entries to the various livestock competitions were up, eighty trade stands were present, and there were sports events in the evening.

Over the last forty years or so, the Driffield Show has gone from strength to strength, and is now considered to be the premier one-day show in the country, with average annual attendances in recent years of 22,500 people. The Society has become very much a business in its own right, and has evolved a complex structure which reflects its continuing success and expanding range of activities.

The Society's governing body is now the General Committee, elected at the Annual General Meeting. This 54-member body elects a President and Chairman annually, and is responsible for appointing the two part-time paid employees of the Society (the Show Director and Assistant, whose remit is to organise the Show and other events and service the Society's 1,700 membership). From the membership of the General Committee, two further committees are elected: the 11-member Management Committee and the 13-member Education Committee, both of which report to the parent body. In addition, there is a trading company called Driffield Showground Ltd. The Society received charitable status in July 1998.

The present objectives of the Society can be summarised as:

1. The furtherance, welfare and progress of the agricultural industry and all trades, crafts and professions connected with it.

2. To encourage and extend, by means of grants or otherwise, agricultural education.

3. To provide for and promote the interests of persons

and organisations involved in agriculture in the area of Driffield, East Yorkshire; to ensure that high professional standards are maintained by members of the agricultural industry and to regulate standards of training of prospective members of the industry; to provide for the delivery and holding of seminars, lectures, discussions, exhibitions, public meetings and conferences for the purpose of enlightening and educating members of the agricultural community in the area of Driffield and the general public; to organise and stage agricultural shows and events of all types.

Further improvements have been made to the showground since 1953, including the provision of toilets, water, electricity and telephone services, and permanent accommodation, as well as facilities for members'. As the Show is only a one-day event, the site has increasingly become the venue for a range of other activities throughout the year. From the beginning, parts of the ground were let as summer grazing, as well as for the use of the Driffield Rugby Union Football Club. In more recent times, a variety of organisations have used the showground facilities for the staging of events, for example, assorted caravan clubs, the British Show Jumping Association, and the Royal Society for the Prevention of Cruelty to Animals. Regular events include the East Yorkshire Country Fair, gun dog trials, steam engine rallies, Truckfest, and meetings of the People in Pigs organisation.

Over the years, the Driffield Show has maintained its traditional agricultural emphasis, but has, in addition, adapted and developed to meet the needs of an ever more diverse group of showgoers, and now includes, amongst other attractions, handicraft and horticultural sections and retail stands. Both the Society and the Show are thriving institutions and are well-placed to meet the challenges and opportunities of the twenty-first century.

19. The 122nd. Driffield Show, Wednesday 17 July 1996.

11. The Yorkshire Wolds waggon

There are few crafts which demonstrate the uniqueness of rural traditions more eloquently than the multiplicity of designs found among historic farm waggons. In such a small geographical area as England, it is surprising that, during the nineteenth and earlier twentieth centuries, so many variations on the same theme could be devised. Although the essential design elements were the same everywhere, individual localities - counties or regions - introduced distinctively local traits, which immediately differentiated the waggons of, for example, the Chilterns from those of the Yorkshire Wolds.

The earliest, rather uncomplimentary, documentary description of the Wolds waggon (*Waud Weggin*) appears to date from the first years of the nineteenth century:

Little can be said in favour of the waggons which are in general use here; they are high, narrow, and long; an inconvenient form for the purposes for which they are intended, that of carrying a top-load, particularly in such parts of the country as are irregular; and they have but one peculiarity in their construction which seems worthy of more general adoption. There is a strong chain on each side of the waggon, of which one end is fixed to the back of the fore-axletree, and the other to the under-side of the body, of such a length as just to prevent the opposite wheel from locking against the side of the waggon in turning; by which means the body may be set much lower between the wheels, without being weakened by cutting the side to admit the wheel (as is sometimes done), and the waggon may be turned within a much smaller space.

The mode of yoking the waggons also, in great part of the East Riding, appears to be a practice nearly peculiar to that district, and is deserving of imitation. The four horses are yoked two abreast, in the same manner as they are put to a coach, two drawing by the splinter-bar and two by the pole; those at the wheel drawing also by a swinging bar, which the wheel-horses of every carriage ought to do, as they thereby obtain considerable ease in their draft, and are less liable to be galled by the collar than those which draw by a fixed bar; the driver then, being mounted on the near-side wheel-horse, directs the two leaders by a rein fixed to the outside of each of their bridles, they being coupled together by a strap passing from the inside of each of their bridles to the collar of the other horse. In this manner, when empty, they trot along the roads with safety and expedition; and when loaded, the horses being near their work, and conveniently placed for drawing, labour with much greater ease and effect than when placed at length. Were the waggon indeed of a better construction, the team would be excellent.

In the making of waggons, too much attention is paid to fashion and the appearance of lightness, to the neglect of strength and utility. He is considered as the best wheel-wright who can pare away his wood to the smallest, and who takes the greatest pain in carving the bodies of his vehicles, to be painted bright blue and scarlet, picked out with black. Waggons are almost universally made with three-inch wheels, and run four feet ten inches wide between the outside of the wheels. It is believed here, that carriages with large axle-trees run easier on ploughed ground, and in deep or heavy roads, than those which have small ones, and as easy on hard level roads; but as many inconveniences and accidents have arisen from the use of wooden axle-trees alone, it has become the practice in the eastern part of the Riding, and perhaps generally so, to let a bar of iron half an inch thick, and two inches broad, into each side of a wooden axle-tree. These extend through the wheel, and about nine inches under the body of the carriage, and are bolted together through the axle-tree; and thus, by the bars standing on edge, give all the strength of an iron axle, without affecting the size of the wooden one.

Technically, the Wolds Waggon was a three-quarter-lock pole waggon, averaging 12 feet in length by 6 feet in width. It stood 6 feet in height, with 5 feet diameter rear wheels and 3 feet diameter fron wheels.

Although many village joiners could, and did, construct these waggons, the principal East Riding manufacturers were Croskills of Beverley (and their successors, the East Yorks Cart and Wagon Co.), and Sissons of Beswick and Cranswick, who were still making them in the 1930s.

In 1900, a Wolds Waggon cost around £40 to buy.

20. Late eighteenth century illustration of a Wolds waggon, reproduced from George Walker's **Costumes of Yorkshire**, 1814.

Despite some obvious differences, the similarities with waggons of one hundred and more years later *(see below)* is very striking.

21 *(left)*. First annual driving competition of the Waggoners' Reserve, with their Wolds waggons, at York Dale, Fimber, 1913.

The Waggoners' Reserve, a corps of 1,000 drivers, was raised by Lieutenant Colonel Sir Mark Sykes (1879-1919), 6th. Baronet, from the Yorkshire Wolds farm workers in 1912, and saw active service during the First World War. Within Sledmere village, opposite the church, is a monument in white Portland stone, sculpted in 1919 by Carlo Magnoni, graphically and idiosyncratically commemorating their war service.

22 *(right)*. Wolds waggon and team of two horses, c.1920-30. Note the small front wheels, designed to lock under the body to give a small turning circle, the use of varnish rather than paint on the waggon body, the panelled front board, and a draught pole instead of shafts.

23 *(left)*. Wolds waggon and team of two horses, c.1920-30. Of all the different types of harness, those used with waggon teams were the most elaborate: in particular, they had a special back-band to hold up the reins, and breechings (britchings) around the horse's hindquarters. The breechings connected, via the collar, to the front of the draught pole, an arrangement which allowed the horses to push the waggon backwards as well as pull it forwards. This provided the only effective means of braking a waggon - though, when descending slopes, the rear wheels were locked by chains and a skid was placed under them to prevent wear and damage.

24 *(right)*. Wolds waggon and team of four horses, yoked as two pairs, at Cowlam Farm, c.1930-35, with waggoner riding postillion.

25 *(left)*. Wolds waggon leaving Driffield with a load of cattle cake, c.1920. The horse team is harnessed in unicorn fashion. The middle horse walked ahead of the pair abreast and was attached with a set of swingletrees and chain to the draught pole. The main problem with this type of arrangement was that there was no way of equalising the draught of the middle horse.

26 *(right)*. Until the demise of the Leicester wool flocks in 1943, this would have been a familiar sight in the district: Wolds waggons of the wool train leaving Driffield, along York Road, c.1913.

12. Horses on the land

Although wind, water and steam could be utilised, heavy horses provided the main source of power for practically all farm work from the eighteenth century up until the Second World War. The increased use of horses, especially from the nineteenth century onwards, arose from the intensification of cultivation, associated with the agricultural revolution, which required more work to be done on the land, and from the use of new implements and machinery, most of which replaced manual labour with horse power.

In 1812, there were 800,000 horses on British farms, by 1870 it had risen to 966,000, by 1887 to 1,034,000, and by 1910 to 1,137,000. Thereafter, the numbers began to decline, at first steadily and then more rapidly, as mechanisation became increasingly prominent. By 1958, when the Ministry of Agriculture took its last census, there were only 84,000 farm horses actively working. The national decline is mirrored in the East Riding: in 1910, there were 27,000 working farm horses, 24,000 in 1920, 22,000 in 1930, 18,000 in 1940, 6,000 in 1950, and 2,000 in 1960.

Up to the end of the nineteenth century, the preferred East Riding farm horse was the Shire; crossbreeds were also common. Usually, only stallions had a pedigree. In the twentieth century, Clydesdales were popular, and, after the First World War, Percherons became a relatively frequent sight in the fields of the district, presumably because soldiers on the Western Front had become acquainted with the merits of the breed.

27. Brood mares and foals in the foldyard at Brigham House Farm, Brigham, c.1910. The clean, fresh state of the foldyard straw would indicate that the photograph was taken during the summer months. Mares were usually worked more or less up to the time they were due to foal.

28. All geared up and ready for the day's work: a posed photograph of the horselads with their teams at Brigham House Farm, c.1910. The horses are clearly in tackle for field work, rather than for hauling waggons. This image also clearly shows the distinctive dress of farm workers prior to 1914. The foreman is Joseph Pledger, who stands at the extreme *left*, with the waggoner next to him. Note the well-maintained farm buildings behind the horses. At this time, the 340 acre Brigham House Farm belonged to the Sledmere estate and was tenanted by Francis Johnson, who employed fourteen workers on the holding.

29. Horselad (a Mr. Robinson) and his team, Brigham House Farm, c.1910. This is a most interesting and unusual photograph: the horses are on their way home at the end of the working day (note the soil on the road around their hooves, where they have been standing for some minutes whilst the photograph was taken), probably, from the background vegetation and possible straw on the roadside verge, in late summer or early autumn. Both horses are lean and not in peak condition; the animal on the left is particularly emaciated, with rib and pelvic bones clearly visible (if the photograph was taken in August-September-October, their condition is particularly unusual, given the plentiful supplies of food over the summer months). Also, only three hooves appear to be shod (front right on the left horse, and both the front hooves of the horse to the right); there are no shoes on either animals' rear hooves; and their hooves, in general, are in poor condition, over-long, cracked, and chipped along the lower edges. Both horses are wearing old and worn collars and bridles - note the angle of the left blinker, or blinder, on the right horse, which, in that position, would not have served any useful purpose. The horse on the right also has reins tied up alongside the collar. The team have obviously been working (matted and dirty feathers), and, given the lack of other gearing, were probably ploughing stubbles or grass prior to the photograph being taken, tasks which normally began in September or October. Does the photograph show the least lad, who, traditionally, was given the worst horses and the worst gearing? Or is there some other explanation to account for the condition of the horses?

30. Day's end and a welcome drink in the pond at Bishop Burton, c.1920-30.

13. Autumn and winter work

31 *(left)*. The basic farming activity of the autumn and winter months was ploughing. This image depicts a six-ox team with a wooden swing plough. Swing ploughs had no wheels and were designed to balance around the body, and the implement was guided by the ploughman, who kept the depth constant by leverage on the long handles. The quality of the resultant work was entirely dependent on the skill and concentration of the ploughman. Although this 1897 photograph was taken on the South Downs, ox-teams would have been a familiar sight in the East Riding, particularly on the heavy claylands, for many centuries.

32 *(right)*. Ploughing with a single furrow, iron-wheeled plough, East Yorkshire, 1920s. Plough harnessing was the simplest type of gearing on farms, and consisted of a collar, chain traces to pull the plough, and a plough back-band to prevent the traces getting caught up in the horses' hind legs. On some farms, back-bands were not used. There is no decoration on the horses' harnesses when employed in field work.

Yorkshire Ploughboy's Song
(Traditional)

Early yan mornin' at t break o' the day
The cocks they was crawin', an' the farmer did say:
"Arise mah good fellers, arise wi' good will.
Yer hosses wants summat their bellies ti fill,

It's past fower o clock lads, so leeak sharp an' rise."
So intiv the stable we merrily flies,
Ti start brushing and wisping
Ti clean, fother, an' muck out, I'll swear an' I'll voo
That we're all jolly fellers what follers the ploo.

When six o'clock comes lads at breakfast we meet,
Beef, breead or fat bacon we put oot o' sight,
With a bit iv oor pockets away we will go
Ti see which on us the best furrow can row.

At neeght t'maister cums roond an to us he did say:
"What hav you been doing lads, all this lang day?
You've nut plooed half a yakker; I'll swear an' I'll vow
You're all idle fellers that follers the ploo!"

I stands up tiv him an' maks this reply:
"We've all plooed a yakker, so you re telling a lie.
We've all plooed a yakker, an' I'll swear an' I'll voo
That we're all honest fellers what follers the ploo."

Oor maister tonned roond, an' laughed at the joke,
Saying "It's past fahve o clock, lads, time ti unyoke.

Lowse oot yer hosses an' rub 'em doon well,
An' Ah'll stand you a jug of real stingo yal."

Noo all you brave ploo lads, wherivver ye be,
Tak this advice, an' be ruled by me,
Deean t fear yer maisters, for I swear an' I voo
We're all honest, jolly fellers what follers the ploo.

33. Ploughing, East Yorkshire, 1920s. The elaborately decorated harnesses suggests that this was a specially posed photograph.

34 *(left)*. A fine photograph of a plough team in action, East Yorkshire, c.1920s-30s.

35 *(right)*. Three single-furrow plough teams working at Brigham House Farm, c.1910. All plough teams on a farm were usually sent out to work together, one behind the other. This was known as fox-hunting. No plough back-bands are in use (see photograph 32). If no further plough teams are operating beyond the edge of the photograph, then this group is ploughing 3 furrows on each run down the field. Note the distinctive pre-1914 dress of the horselads. Even so, there was still some room for individuality: one lad wears a cap, whilst the others are sporting raddy-doo hats, which, in cold weather, could be pulled down over the ears.

36. Posed photograph of a plough team at work on heavy clay at Manor Farm, Dunnington, in northern Holderness, c.1940. The image depicts an iron-wheeled plough. According to how they were set by the ploughman, the wheels on the implement controlled both the width and the depth of the furrow. The large wheel (left) ran in the furrow and the horizontal distance between it and the plough coulter determined the width of the turned furrow. The vertical distance between this wheel's lowest point and that of its smaller counterpart on the unploughed land determined the depth of the furrow cut by the plough.

Cultivating by steam

The early origins of steam ploughing can probably be traced back to 1619, when James I gave a patent to David Ramsey and Thomas Wildgoose:

Who have by theire industrye, and att theire great paynes, costs, charges and expences, devised, found out, and brought to pfeccion, divers Newe, Apte, or Compendious Formes or Kind of Engines or Instruments to Ploughe Ground, without Horse or Oxen ... They have the sole privilege of making and using said engines ... Any infringement will be defaced, thrown down, destroyed and broken ...

The modern history of steam ploughing began in the 1830s, precipitated by a period of agricultural prosperity. In 1832, John Heathcoat and Josiah Parkes patented a steam engine, consisting of a low platform and two winding drums, capable of hauling a plough across a field on an endless chain.

In 1846, John Tulloh Osborn patented the idea of the first two-engined steam ploughing tackle. Two engines, each with a vertical side-winding drum upon which long chains were coiled, were stationed at opposite sides of the field and the plough was hauled across the intervening space from one engine to the other.

This basic idea was refined throughout the middle decades of the nineteenth century by, most notably, John Fowler of Leeds, who was responsible for firmly establishing the steam plough, both in production and use, as a facet of cultivation.

In the East Riding, steam cultivation was generally restricted to the heavy and deep soils of the lowland districts. Because of the high costs involved in the purchase of equipment, placing it beyond the reach of all but the most wealthy farmers, cultivation by steam-powered engines was normally undertaken by contractors, such as John Hardbattle and Son of Aldborough, who operated throughout Holderness in the 1880s, 1890s and beyond.

A set of steam tackle consisted of two self-powered engines, a cultivator, a balanced plough, harrows, a two-wheeled 250 gallon water cart, and a double boarded sleeping van, in which the crew ate and slept when travelling between farms. In 1870, a set of tackle, manufactured by John Fowler and Co. of Leeds, cost £1,600. Other manufacturers included J. and F. Howard of Bedford, Aveling and Porter of Rochester, Charles Burrell and Co. of Thetford, and Savage Brothers of King's Lynn.

The operating gang comprised a foreman, two drivers, a steersman, steersman's mate, and a cook. Usually, the gangs, leading a semi-nomadic existence for much of the year, were paid weekly; they also earned an acreage bonus of a few pence per acre for the work accomplished by their set.

Coal and water, for power, were provided by the farmer to whom the set was contracted.

In the late nineteenth century, the hire of a steam set cost, typically, 14s. per acre for ploughing and £1 per acre for cultivating twice over.

On a good day, *when everything went right*, a steam set could work 50 acres of land with a cultivator.

37. Steam ploughing at Sunk Island, Holderness, c.1920-30, with a Fowler model BB1 16 nominal horse-power compound ploughing engine drawing a Fowler six-furrow general purpose anti-balance plough.

38. 1980s demonstration of steam ploughing at Manor Farm, Kelk, with *Dreadnought*, a Fowler model BB1 16 nominal horse-power compound ploughing engine, manufactured in 1925, and a Fowler four-furrow semi-digger anti-balance plough.

39 *(left)*. From the late 1940s, tractors became an increasingly common sight in the fields of the East Riding. This is a Standard Fordson tractor and two-furrow mounted plough at work on the Yorkshire Wolds during the late 1940s, possibly at a Young Farmers' ploughing match.

40 *(right)*. Ploughing with a Fordson tractor and three-furrow trailed plough on the Yorkshire Wolds during the later 1940s. This photograph was taken at a ploughing match (note the identification sticker on the front of the tractor).

41. Case tractor and plough on stubbles, Yorkshire Wolds, c.1950.

42 *(left)*. Platypus 30 caterpillar tractor, with a Perkins P4 diesel engine rated at 39 horse-power, and Ransome five-furrow plough, Kirkburn Manor Farm, c.1954.

43 *(right)*. This evocative photograph shows two Massey Ferguson 65 tractors and four-furrow Ransome ploughs working at Littlethorpe Farm, Rudston, c.1965.

44 *(left)*. Bray Centaur experimental unit with push-pull left and right hand plough, Watton Grange Farm, Watton, 1960s.

45 *(right)*. Experimental combined plough and tractor, Watton Grange Farm, 1960s.

46. *When Arthur and Lancelot met the CAT*. Photograph of the two extremes of ploughing. On the right, a two-ox team (*Arthur* and *Lancelot*) and wooden beam plough, capable of ploughing, depending on local conditions, 1 acre per day to a depth of 4 inches. Such a team - with perhaps four, six or eight oxen - would have been a familiar sight on the heavy, intractable clays of lowland East Yorkshire from the medieval period up to the nineteenth century; on the lighter soils of the Wolds, horses were used at least from the sixteenth century. On the left is an example of modern agricultural technology: a 1998 230 horse-power Caterpillar diesel tractor and eight-furrow reversible plough, capable of ploughing 50 acres per day to a depth of 8 inches.

47 *(left)*. A posed group of female potato harvesters at Bracken Farm, Kilnwick, near Driffield, 1941. Note the varied ages of the group and their dress. Up until the 1960s, the potato harvest was a labour intensive activity. Behind the group is a heavy horse and a two-wheeled cart with shafts.

48 *(right)*. Potato harvesting at Dunnington, near York, in the late 1950s/early 1960s.

49. Potato harvesting, eastern England, late 1950s/early 1960s. Here, the actual work of picking the crop is being undertaken by schoolboys, possibly during the autumn half-term holiday.

50 *(left)*. The field-edge storage of lifted potatoes, eastern England, 1950s. This photograph clearly shows the method of constructing a potato clamp.

51 *(right)*. By the late 1960s/early 1970s, the labour intensive nature of the potato harvest had largely been displaced by the introduction of machinery. This photograph shows a Grimme Gazelle single row potato harvester at Littlethorpe Farm, Rudston, in 1973.

52 *(left)*. Modern potato harvester at work at Southburn, near Driffield, 1990s. Potatoes are lifted between September and October.

53 *(right)*. Tractor cab view of modern potato harvester lifting a crop at Southburn, 1990s.

54 *(left)*. Clearing out the foldyard of its accumulated over-winter straw and manure at Newby Farm, Huggate, c.1937. The cleaning out of foldyards, and the carting and spreading of manure took place between November and March.

55 *(right)*. Muck leading time at Newby Farm, Huggate, c.1937. Note the use of a four-wheeled flat-back trailer, or rully, with draught pole, as opposed to a waggon.

56 *(left)*. Muck spreading near Bishop Burton, 1920s-1930s. This time, a Wolds waggon is in use. From the waggon, rully or cart, the manure was piled into heaps at intervals across the field and then spread manually.

57 *(right)*. Muck spreading at Kirkburn, 1980s.

58. When most farms had only small granaries, the sheaves of cut corn were stacked - in the stackyard - until such time as the grain needed to be threshed. Threshing was a dirty and noisy job, which commonly took place between January and March. As threshing sets, consisting of a portable steam engine, the threshing machine itself, straw elevator, chaff cutter and straw trusser, were expensive to purchase - in 1914, for example, a complete set, depending on its size and specification, cost anywhere between £460 and £1,100 - they were usually operated by contractors. Here, a threshing set is seen arriving at Brigham House Farm, c.1910. The contractor is believed to be William Foley of North Frodingham. The engine is an Aveling and Porter single cylinder six horse-power machine with, possibly, a Ruston threshing set in tow.

59. Early on the day of threshing, the engine driver and his mate would remove all overnight waterproof covers, light the engine's fire, check all lubrication points and oil if necessary, and put all belts on their pulleys. The machinery would be running and ready to start work by 7am. There would be a half hour meal break at about 9.30am, followed by a one hour lunch break, commencing at 12.30pm. The day's work would normally finish at about 5pm. The meal breaks provided the engine driver and his mate with opportunities to check all the machinery, and make whatever adjustments were necessary. This early image of threshing tackle in operation was taken in the Malton district in 1880, and shows a Fowler steam engine and Marshall drum. The double row of staggered strakes on the rear wheel of the engine is indicative of an early date of manufacture. A water bucket is standing alongside the wheel of the engine. The engineer sits on the platform of the machine *(extreme left)*, with, probably, the contractor standing next to him; the man on the threshing set is the engineer's mate, whose job it was to feed the threshing drum. He is flanked by two women workers, who, having received the sheaves from the pitcher on the stack, would cut their bindings and pass them to the feeder. The stack, with the pitcher, is on the *extreme right* of the photograph. Stacks were built with sufficient sheaves for one day's threshing; notice, then, that the stack itself is about one-third threshed, indicating that the photograph was taken towards late morning. All the other staff in the photograph would be from the farm, supplemented, quite possibly, with casual workers employed specifically for the task in hand.

60 *(left)*. A threshing day at Brigham House Farm, c.1910. When in use, the provision of coal and water was the responsibility of the farmer: between 200-250 gallons of water (the farm hand is carrying two pails of water towards the engine) and 8-12cwt. of coal would be used on a single day when threshing. The stack on the *right* is almost finished, and that on the *left* has had its thatch removed in preparation for threshing. The Wolds waggon, with its decorated end-board, appears either to have been freshly painted or recently bought.

Straw was the residue of threshing and would have been turned into farmyard manure by the livestock and then returned to the land - an essential element in maintaining soil fertility before the advent of modern chemical fertilisers.

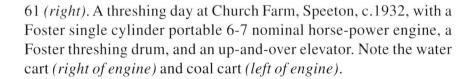

61 *(right)*. A threshing day at Church Farm, Speeton, c.1932, with a Foster single cylinder portable 6-7 nominal horse-power engine, a Foster threshing drum, and an up-and-over elevator. Note the water cart *(right of engine)* and coal cart *(left of engine)*.

62. This very unusual photograph of two threshing sets operating simultaneously in the same stackyard was taken at Haverfield Farm, Patrington, 1932. At the height of the inter-war depression this 814 acre Holderness farm was vacated by the tenant and, subsequently, proved difficult to let. The acreage was, therefore, broken down into smaller units and let to a number of different people. The rather chaotic scene *(above)* shows the stacks of two different farmers being threshed at the same time. The photograph also documents very clearly the division of labour when threshing: (1) the engine driver was responsible for keeping the fire going to ensure steady steam pressure and for the overall running of the machinery; (2) the engine driver's mate fed the threshing drum; and (3) the staff provided by the farmer would undertake various jobs: two men on the corn stack to pitch the sheaves on to the threshing machine *(extreme right and centre)*; one man to cut the bands and pass the sheaves to the feeder *(on threshing machine at left)*; one man to clear chaff and cavings *(left)*; several men carrying the sacks of threshed grain *(extreme left)*; if an elevator was in use, there would be two or three men on the straw stack; if a baler was in use, two men would make the bales and one would stack *(foreground)*; if a chaff cutter was in use, one man fed the machine, one man removed the sacks, and one man stacked or loaded the sacks; if a trusser was in use, one or two men pitched and two men on stack. The contractors in this photograph are Burnham of Burstwick *(left)* and Wilkin of Welwick *(right)*.

63. *lowance* time during a threshing day at Kilnwick Hall Farm, Kilnwick, near Driffield, c.1928-31. *Back row, left to right*: Frank Botham, Harold Harrison, J. Knowles, Joshua Pickering, Jack Brant A. Hoggard, Tom Harrison and Fred Suggitt (farm foreman). *Front row, left to right:* George Harper, Bill Pickering, Jess Suggitt, Horace Harrison and Tom Dunnington.

64 *(left)*. Threshing at Church Farm, Speeton, c.1940-41. Note the use of a Fordson tractor to provide the power for the threshing drum.

65 *(right)*. Threshing set belonging to contractor J. Knowles leaving Kilnwick Hall Farm, c.1928-31. When work on the farm was completed, it was usually arranged with the farmer that the tackle would depart with at least sufficient coal and water to get to the next farm. The engine is a 6 nominal horse-power single cylinder Marshall, with a Marshall threshing set and elevator in tow.

66. Two three-horse teams harrowing with broad zig-zag harrows, eastern England, 1930s. After ploughing, the winter frosts were allowed to break down the field surface and kill the weeds. Then, it was necessary to break up the furrow pattern to create a smooth seed bed by harrowing. Note that the horses are not wearing back-bands, and that they are harnessed by individual drawbars, rather than multiple swingletrees for working abreast.

67 *(left)*. Harrowing with a two-horse team at Castle Farm, Sledmere, c.1920-30. Note that the horses are, in this photograph, wearing back-bands.

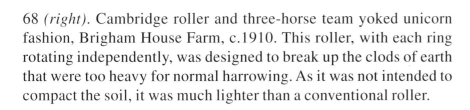

68 *(right)*. Cambridge roller and three-horse team yoked unicorn fashion, Brigham House Farm, c.1910. This roller, with each ring rotating independently, was designed to break up the clods of earth that were too heavy for normal harrowing. As it was not intended to compact the soil, it was much lighter than a conventional roller.

69 *(left)*. Massey Ferguson 65 tractor and spring tine cultivator preparing a seed bed at Littlethorpe Farm, Rudston, c.1965-66.

70 *(right)*. Massey Ferguson 1200 110 horse-power tractor and harrows, Abbey Farm, Watton, 1972. This was the first specially designed four-wheel drive tractor, and whose safety cab was an integral part of the machine.

71 *(left)*. Ford FW-60 tractor and set of Simba 2-3C discs in operation at Kirkburn Manor Farm, 1997.

72 *(right)*. Seed bed preparation at Southburn, late 1990s. Case International Harvester 130 horse-power tractor and push-pull Farm Force 6mm. harrows.

73. Once the seed bed was prepared, the seed was sown using a drill, which cut small grooves into which the seed was dropped at regular intervals across the field surface. This photograph was taken at Enholmes Farm, Patrington in the 1920s. The lad at the front is leading the horses *without* reins, but, as the lines of seed had to be sown perfectly straight, a man *(second from left)* guides the horse in shafts with a pole in order to keep the drill exactly on course. Another man, *standing behind the drill's right wheel*, watches the drill coulters and ensures that blockages do not create bare patches where no seed has been sown - this task was often undertaken by the farm foreman or a more experienced hand. The man *standing immediately behind the drill* is probably the farmer.

74. Sowing, eastern England, c.1930-40. These drills, with their three-horse teams, are probably turnip drills as they have four double coulters, which sowed seed and fertiliser simultaneously.

75 *(left)*. Bettinson 3D direct drill at Grange Farm, Watton, late 1960s/early 1970s. This machine drilled direct into stubbles, and was often used to establish fodder turnip crops or wheat crops after a good straw burn.

76 *(right)*. Massey Ferguson 500 seed drill in operation at Southburn, 1990s.

77 *(left)*. A fine Yorkshire Wolds landscape photograph, showing seed bed preparation at Dotterill Park Farm, Kilham, c.1946-47.

78 *(right)*. Fordson Major tractor and three flat rollers rolling cereals, after drilling, at Littlethorpe Farm, Rudston, 1953-54.

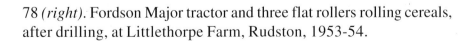

79 *(left)*. With the demise of the great sheep flocks during the Second World War, potatoes gradually replaced turnips as the main root crop. The sequence of seed bed preparation for potatoes is as follows: the land is first ploughed, then formed into ridges, followed by de-stoning in order to avoid abrasion to the growing crop, and then finally the seed potatoes are planted. These operations take place between February and May. This photograph shows seed bed preparation for potatoes at Fimber Nab Farm, Sledmere, 1990s. A John Deere 8100 tractor and Lely bed former are at work.

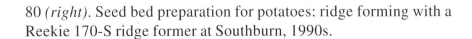
80 *(right)*. Seed bed preparation for potatoes: ridge forming with a Reekie 170-S ridge former at Southburn, 1990s.

81 *(left)*. Seed bed preparation for potatoes: destoning with a Reekie 330 de-stoner and Case International tractor at Southburn, 1990s.

82 *(right)*. Seed potatoes transferred to the potato planter at Fimber Nab Farm, 1990s.

83 *(left)*. Potato planting at Southburn, 1998, with a Key AGG two-row planter.

84 *(right)*. A fine photograph of potato seed bed preparation and planting, taken at Fimber Nab Farm, 1990s. At the *rear*, a ridge former, in the *centre* two Grimme de-stoners, and at the *front* a Grimme planter in operation, hauled by three John Deere and one Massey Ferguson tractors.

14. Spring work

85. Early crop spraying with horse-drawn sprayers, eastern England, 1930s. Note the lack of protection.

86. Early crop spraying with a tractor, eastern England, c.1930-40.

87 *(left)*. Crop spraying with a Ford Super Major tractor at Grange Farm, Watton, late 1950s/early 1960s.

88 *(right)*. Aerial crop spraying at Littlethorpe Farm, Rudston, c.1962.

89 *(left)*. Crop spraying with a Ford 5000 tractor at Abbey Farm, Watton, 1975.

90 *(right)*. Modern crop spraying with a Chafer Tramline sprayer, which could apply chemicals or liquid fertiliser. This machine had several advanced features: tramline tracking, boom suspension, and electronic controls. Photograph taken in the East Riding, c.1990s, spraying liquid fertiliser or fungicide on to winter wheat.

91. Self-propelled HS Sprint 2000 crop sprayer, with a 24 metre boom length, at work on the Yorkshire Wolds during the 1990s. This photograph shows the spraying of winter wheat against crop disease.

92. A busy hay-making scene in the park at Sledmere, late nineteenth century, with the south-facing front of Sledmere House forming the backdrop. The mowing machine began to make its appearance from the 1880s, but its introduction was uneven. Here, with the exception of the carting, all the work is being undertaken manually. Hay-making was one of the few occasions on the farm when the different sections of the workforce genuinely mixed together at the same task. There were so few jobs for horses and the requirement was for plenty of manual labour in order to get the hay made before it was spoiled by adverse weather conditions. When a lot of hay was made, extra hands would be hired. Many of the workers in this photograph are wearing broad-brimmed hats, which provided shade and kept the midges off. No worker has more than his forearms exposed - anything more would have been regarded as unseemly, even for work as hot as this.

93 *(left)*. Hay-making at Brigham House Farm, c.1910. A posed photograph of a group of hay-makers standing in front of a horse-drawn mowing machine. The mower left the grass in swathes, which would then be turned by hand with wooden rakes while it dried. It was then pulled into larger swathes, and then gathered into heaps. Finally, it would be gathered up and taken to the farm, where it would be stacked and protected from the weather by a covering of thatch.

94 *(right)*. Mowing grass in eastern England, 1930s.

95 *(left)*. Mowing grass at Skerne Leys, near Driffield, 1939.

96 *(right)*. Grass cutting with a mower-crimper at Grange Farm, Watton, mid-1970s.

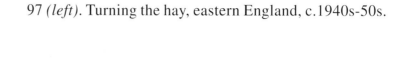

97 *(left)*. Turning the hay, eastern England, c.1940s-50s.

98 *(right)*. Leading hay, Flamborough, c.1920s-30s.

99 *(left)*. Hay stacks under construction, Brigham House Farm, c.1910.

100 *(right)*. A wedge-shaped silage clamp under construction at Littlethorpe Farm, Rudston, late 1950s or early 1960s. The tractor consolidating the clamp is an early Fordson Dexter.

15. Summer work

101 *(left)*. The widespread cultivation of vining peas is a relatively recent introduction into the East Riding, which is regarded as a most favourable area for their growing on account of the cool climate. Vining commences in July with the harvesting of peas for freezing. Here, a contractor's Ploeger EPD-520 pea viner, costing £250,000, is in operation at Southburn, 1990s.

102 *(right)*. A Ploeger EPD-520 pea viner transferring its load to a trailer, Southburn, 1990s. Harvested peas must be taken to the factory at Hessle, washed, prepared and frozen within 90 minutes of being harvested.

Harvest Time

The first point to be made about nineteenth century harvesting is that it was an immense and communal activity, involving more workers than ever before or since. This was partly because of the growth of population; partly because farms were larger, crop yields heavier, and landless labourers more numerous; above all, because the work of the human arm was still of far greater importance than that of the machine. The 1851 national population census gives a figure of 1,077,627 agricultural workers in England and Scotland. But the number of people in the harvest fields was certainly more, because at harvest time the Victorian farmer relied not only on his regular workforce, but also on their wives and their children, on migrants from Ireland and other parts of the British Isles, and on local casual workers.

In harvest time, the work was physically hard. As Richard Jefferies wrote in 1889, when describing the harvest scene in southern England:

Next day the village sent forth its army with their crooked weapons to cut and slay ... More men and more men were put on day by day, and women to bind the sheaves ... as the wheat fell, the shocks [stooks] rose behind them, low tents of corn. Your skin or mine could not have stood the scratching of the straw, which is stiff and sharp, and the burning of the sun, which blisters like red-hot iron. No one could stand the harvest-field as a reaper except he had been born [to it] ... Their necks grew black ... Their open chests were always bare, and flat, and stark ... The breast bone was burned black, and their arms, tough as ash, seemed cased in leather. They grew visibly thinner in the harvest-field, and shrunk together - all flesh disappearing, and nothing but sinew and muscle remaining. Never was such work ... So they worked and slaved, and tore at the wheat ... the heat, the aches, the illness, the sunstroke, always impending in the air - the stomach hungry again before the meal was over ... No song, no laugh, no stay - on from morn till night ...

There were many more tasks in the harvest fields than could be performed by the regularly employed farm labour force, and extra hands were needed from the time the corn was cut to the time when the last bolt of straw had been carried to the thatcher and the last stack constructed. Cutting could still be going on in one field, while, in another, already cut corn was being stooked or carted away. Wheat might be ready to cart in a matter of days; oats, it was considered, should stand in stook for three Sundays. Barley had to be turned like hay in the swathe, because, unlike wheat, it retained sap in the straw, so carrying had to wait on wilting, especially in the case of undersown barley. No single group of workers could perform all the harvest tasks, for their demands inevitably clashed. There was a continuous succession of work for all available hands - children and women helping to make bands and binding and stooking; men cutting and carting; women raking the ground behind. The younger men pitched to the waggon, and from waggon to stack, for this was regarded as the most strenuous of work; older men often worked at loading the waggons or building the stacks, where their experience was valued and their strength less taxed.

Each task was urgent. The corn, once cut, could not be left unsheaved overnight: the sheaved corn could not be left uncarted when ripe for risk of shedding. *A field of wheat left uncut a day too long may have two bushels an acre blown out of it by a high wind ... barley left uncarted ... changed from good malting sample to cheap feeding stuff.*

Mechanical aids to harvesting were slow to be accepted in English agricultural practice, and the extensive use of hand tools continued right up to the end of the nineteenth century. The mechanical reaper was the first to come into general use, from the 1870s, but was by no means universal, even at the turn of the century. But, by the 1880s, all the aids of modern machine harvesting, with the exception of the combine harvester, were in production. The self-sheaving reaper-binder was now available, as were a variety of horse-drawn machines, including mowers, stacking machines and elevators.

The gradual introduction of the machine mower and the machine reaper with its *splendidly painted sails* was, in principle, no different from the continuous process of speeding up the harvest which had been going on for many years. It changed the balance of labour in the harvest field, but only partially. Labour in the first stage of harvest - the cutting - was drastically curtailed. But there was still ample work available: tying, sheaving and carting. There was much less work, however, for migrant harvesters, but the employment of women and children and extra hands drawn from the locality was not affected. Moreover, the introduction of machine reapers coincided with, though it did not cause, the beginning of rural depopulation, so its impact on the rural labour market was, to some extent, cushioned.

The mechanical reaper-binder effected a much more drastic change. It eliminated those branches of harvest work that had been the chief employment of women and children - the making and tying of sheaves. At a stroke, it destroyed the *double wage* - the family working unit that had been the basis of high harvest earnings.

The introduction of the mechanical reaper and binder transformed the harvest situation to the advantage of the regular agricultural servant. As regards the ordinary farm staff, no labour was dispensed with, but for the unattached worker - and for all those villagers who had been accustomed to take up field work at harvest time - it was quite otherwise. Casual labour, whether specialist or local, was no longer wanted; there was no longer a need for a large migrant labour force, or for the village populations to take to the fields at harvest time. Farmers were able to put the opportunity of extra harvest earnings in the way of their regular employees, and the labour and account books of the period begin to record special payments against their names instead of against those of outsiders. Overtime payments took the place of piece-rate jobs. Regular farm servants were now used in all stages of the harvest. Family labour was dispensed with. The farm workforce became more fixed. The independent villager's position was undermined. There was more regular employment, but it went with a growing dependence on the farmer all the year round.

103. Harvesting in eastern Yorkshire, c.1870. This early, and striking, photograph shows people working in a field of oats in the later nineteenth century. It illustrates the first three operations in the cereal harvest and points to a precise division of labour. The *rat trap* mowing machines, each drawn by two horses and operated by one man each *(centre left and right)* have displaced hand-cutting, thus dispensing with the labour of several men using either hooks or scythes. The women's work is to make bands (into the strands in the hands of the two women to the *left*) and then gather and tie the loose corn into sheaves (women on the *far right*). The men are following behind, picking up and forming the sheaves into stooks; in the background, men can be seen amongst those sheaves already set up. Some of the sheaves towards the back of the field have yet to be set up, and the machines still have part of the crop to cut. Although it is probable that some of the women were the wives of some of the men, they were not, as such, working with them, but formed a separate team or gang, and were probably paid a rate per acre for this work, to be divided equally between them. Similarly, it is probable that the men worked as a team stooking the corn at so much per acre, again to be divided equally. As regards the mowing machine operators, they were probably waggoners and, although paid at normal rates, they would have received an additional harvest sum.

104 *(left)*. Binder, with a three-horse team harnessed in unicorn fashion, working at Brigham House Farm, c.1910. This Massey Harris No.5 binder was available with either a 5ft. or 6ft. cut, right or left hand, and cost £37 in 1910.

105 *(right)*. A four-horse team harvesting on the Yorkshire Wolds during the 1930s. It would have been a heavy wheat crop that needed four horses on the binder. At this time, a good wheat yield would be around 18cwt. per acre, and the most popular varieties were: Yeoman, Victor, Square Head's Master, Standard Red, Little Joss, Swedish Iron and Rivet.

106 *(left)*. Harvesting at Skerne, 1938.

107 *(right)*. Case International W30 tractor and McCormick 8ft. binder at Cawkeld Farm, Kilnwick, 1940.

108 *(left)*. Two Case International W30 tractors and McCormick 8ft. binders at work on Cawkeld Farm, Kilnwick, 1942.

109 *(right)*. Harvesting at Church Farm, Speeton, 1944.

110 *(left)*. Stooking wheat at Cawkeld Farm, Kilnwick, c.1940-42. The sheaves stood in stooks of ten or twelve to dry.

111 *(right)*. A typical harvest scene: a field of stooked sheaves awaiting removal to the stackyard, eastern England, c.1930-40.

112 *(left). Old meets new.* An interesting and evocative harvest scene, photographed at Church Farm, Speeton, in 1946, during the transition from horse-power to mechanisation.

113 *(right).* Leading stooks at Sledmere Grange Farm, September 1961.

114 *(left)*. Harvest home: a waggon load of sheaves entering a stackyard at Lund, 1940s. Note the detachable raised side boards on the waggon; they were used when it was necessary to keep a high load secure.

115 *(right)*. Stacking corn at Church Farm, Speeton, 1939-40.

116 *(left)*. Constructing a pike stack at Brigham House Farm, c.1910. Pikes were round, constructed from wheat sheaves, and were very popular in the East Riding. Note the use of a Monkey, a wooden platform resting against the side of the stack in order for the builders to gain height for the stacking process.

117 *(right)*. Row of neatly thatched pike stacks in the stackyard at Hall Garth Farm, Leven, c.1920s-30s. The round pikes were considered to be showcase examples of the stackers' art. The last course of thatch laid on this type of stack was called a *Mopin*, and this drew the stack to a point. Stacks were thatched - or roofed -in order to keep the rain from destroying the collected crop. Stack thatching was a very skilled operation.

118. This fine picturesque photograph of a stackyard scene was taken in the Luttons-Heslerton area between 1945-50, and is a striking example of the stack-maker's skill. On the extreme *left* is a humble-end stack. These were plain in appearance, had no corners, and were considered the simplest form of stack to construct. The simplicity of their construction made them ideal for barley sheaves, which were inclined to slip, making their stacking difficult. Next is a gable-end stack, so named because of its similarity to houses of that type. On the *right*, the stackyard is dominated by rows of pikes. Each stack usually contained sufficient sheaves for one day's threshing.

119 *(left)*. An early trailed Claas bagger combine with baler attachment, hauled by a Standard Fordson tractor, at work in a wheat crop, Littlethorpe Farm, Rudston, c.1953-55.

120 *(right)*. The same equipment, location and date as depicted in photograph 119, *above*.

121 *(left)*. A self-propelled Massey Harris 21 bagger combine at work in a field of oats in the Driffield area, September 1946.

122 *(right)*. A self-propelled Massey Harris 780 combine, Kirkburn Manor Farm, late 1950s/early 1960s.

123 *(left)*. A self-propelled Claas Matador Standard tank combine off-loading into a trailer, hauled by a TEA 20 30 horse-power tractor, at Littlethorpe Farm, Rudston, early to mid 1960s.

124 *(right)*. Harvesting with a Massey Ferguson 400 series combine at Kirkburn Manor Farm, late 1960s/early 1970s.

125 *(left)*. Three Claas Dominator combine harvesters abreast at Southburn, August 1998. Each machine, with its 25ft. cut and advanced computer system for monitoring, for example, grain moisture content and tonnage per acre, is capable of combining 80 acres per day. In the 1990s, cereal yields could be between 3 and 4 tons per acre.

126 *(right)*. A Claas 218 Dominator combine harvester at work at Southburn, 1995.

127 (left). Two New Holland TX66 combine harvester with straw-chopping attachments, Fimber Nab Farm, Sledmere, 1997.

128 (right). Baling at Kirkburn Manor Farm, early 1970s, with a Massey Ferguson 65, Mk. 2, tractor and McCormick International B-46 baler and Perry bale collector.

129 *(left)*. Baling at Littlethorpe Farm, Rudston, c.1963-65, with a Welger baler and bale delivery-shoot for stacking directly on to a trailer

130 *(right)*. Baling, eastern Yorkshire, 1985, with auto-stacker bale sledge, capable of stacking 12-16 bales and depositing them at one point in the field ready for collection.

131. Baling with a Case 7250 tractor and New Holland D1000 baler,
Kirkburn Manor Farm, 1990s.

16. Livestock

132. The prize-winning Great and Little Kendale Leicester Tup (ram), set against a Wolds background; Driffield is just visible above the dog, *centre left*. An unattributed oil on canvas painting, dating to the later nineteenth century. The ram has an extremely long back and small head and the anatomy in general appears exaggerated, in an almost naïve style. In his 1642 **Farming Book**, Henry Best of Elmswell wrote of a good tup: *Lett him bee large and well quartered, of a snoode and good staple, with a longe and bushie tayle, without hornes, and havinge both stones in the codde; and lastly, neaver under two sheare, nor seldome above five; for beinge over younge, theire bloode is hotte and the scabbe is procured, and beinge over olde their radicall moisture is wasted.*

133 *(left)*. Folded Leicester longwool sheep at Brigham House Farm, c.1910. From the earlier nineteenth century up to the 1940s, Leicester sheep dominated the livestock scene in the East Riding, particularly on the Wolds, and formed an essential element in the Mixed Farming regime practised at that time. They were famed for their long fleeces, which went to the woollen industry in the West Riding. Indeed, such was the demand for these lustrous fleeces and the high monetary value they yielded, that it was not uncommon for the wool cheque to pay the entire yearly rental on many farms. During the 1850-70 period, many farmers made substantial profits from the sale of fleeces, so much so that the accumulated sums were sufficient to cushion them from the severe agricultural depression from the 1880s onwards.

134 *(right)*. Leicester longwool sheep and lambs, Brigham, c.1910.

135 *(left)*. A shepherd standing in the doorway of his mobile shepherd's hut at Brigham House Farm, c.1910, with his dog patiently waiting for orders. Such huts provided living accommodation for the shepherd during lambing time.

136 *(right)*. Sheep washing in the canal at Brigham, c.1910.

137 *(left)*. Sheep washing at Bishop Burton, c.1930-40.

138 *(right)*. Land Army girls sheep clipping with hand shears on the Yorkshire Wolds, 1940s.

139 *(left)*. Sheep shearing competition in the East Riding, late 1940s/early 1950s.

140 *(right)*. The wool bales on a rully with a three-horse team harnessed in unicorn fashion, ready for departure to the railway station. This photograph was taken at Driffield in the earlier part of the twentieth century.

141 *(left). A winter's job:* two farm workers, in their highly distinctive clothes, posing by a turnip cutter, East Riding, late nineteenth century.

142 *(right). Snow on the ground:* feeding turnips to sheep at Church Farm, Speeton, 1957, with a Case tractor and 4-wheeled rully.

143 *(left)*. A herd of dual purpose dairy Shorthorn cows on their way to the milking parlour, Brigham House Farm, c.1910. At this time, each animal would have taken about 20 minutes to milk by hand, and would, when on grass, have produced around 3 gallons per day. Milking would have been undertaken by the beastman, or bullocky, with female assistance provided by the daughters of the farm staff. In general, milk, cream, butter and cheese would have been sold off the farm, providing a useful cash supplement to the farmer's wife's income.

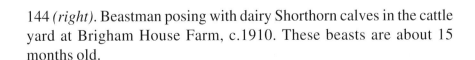

144 *(right)*. Beastman posing with dairy Shorthorn calves in the cattle yard at Brigham House Farm, c.1910. These beasts are about 15 months old.

145. Ayrshires at Towthorpe Dairies, Red House Farm, Middleton-on-the-Wolds, late 1940s. The dairy had a milk round at RAF Driffield, as well as in Driffield itself, and advertised on film at the Victoria cinema in the town. Following trouble with brucellosis, the farm went over to pig production.

146 *(left)*. Yorkshire Wolds farmstead, date unknown. Crossbred beef cattle housed in open yard with straw bale surrounds, and fed on silage or hay. This method of rearing was considered by many to be inefficient.

147 *(right)*. Driffield Cattle Market in the early twentieth century.

148 *(left). Real Yorkshire pigs.* This photograph, taken at Brigham House Farm, c.1910, shows twenty-one pure Middle White piglets, from at least two litters. Middle Whites have short pricked ears and short snouts.

149 *(right).* Beastman with piglets at Brigham House Farm, c.1910. These animals have bigger, floppier ears and larger snouts than Middle Whites, and are probably Large White crossed with Middle White pigs.

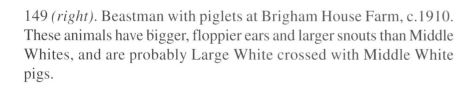

150. Pigs at Enholmes Farm, Patrington, 1950s-60s. Typical open and interconnecting yards with shelter sheds along one side, which could be used for cattle, sheep or pigs. These fat pigs would be living largely on straw and undigested corn in cattle dung.

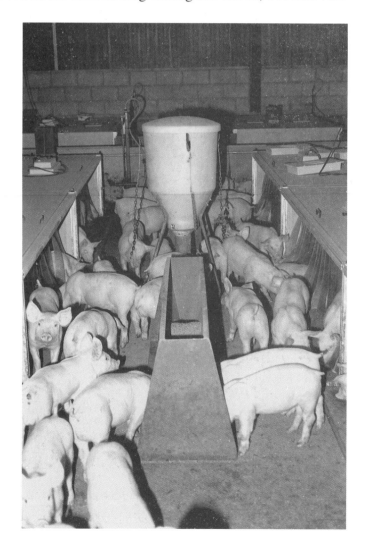

151 *(left)*. Pigs at Enholmes Farm, Patrington, 1960s-70s. This Danish design piggery, used for finishing pigs prior to sale, was common in the East Riding during the 1950s, 60s and 70s.

152 *(right)*. Weaned pigs in kennelled living area, with *ad-lib* feed hoppers and water troughs. This type of accommodation was common in the East Riding during the 1980s-90s.

153 *(left)*. Outdoor pig rearing on the sandy soils at Rillington, on the southern edge of the Vale of Pickering, 1999.

154 *(right)*. Outdoor, crossbred pigs at Rillington, 1999.

17. Farmworkers: some portraits

155 *(left)*. Singling out turnips at Castle Farm, Sledmere, 1920s-30s.

156 *(right)*. This is an interesting photograph of the entire Cowlam farm staff at some date in the 1930s. Although there are echoes of earlier times, the clothing of farmworkers depicted in this image is losing its distinctive character. Some of the lads are obviously wearing hand-me-down clothing, including boots.

157 *(left)*. Undated and unlocated (possibly Middleton-on-the-Wolds area) photograph of farm staff, posing around a wheelbarrow load of mangolds. Pike stacks form the backdrop.

158 *(right)*. Undated photograph of farm staff on the South Dalton estate.

18. Further reading

Unless otherwise stated, the place of publication is London

Allison, K.J., 1976. **The East Riding of Yorkshire Landscape**.

Antrim, Angela, 1981. **The Yorkshire Wold Rangers**. Driffield.

Armstrong, Alan, 1988. **Farmworkers: a social and economic history, 1770-1980**.

Barnwell, P.S. and Giles, C., 1997. **English Farmsteads, 1750-1914**. Swindon.

Barugh, W., 1854. **Master and Man: A Reply to the Agricultural Labourer as He Really Is**. Driffield.

Bonnett, Harold, 1995. **Farming with Steam**. Princes Risborough.

Brigden, Roy, 1998. **Ploughs and Ploughing**. Princes Risborough.

Brown, Jonathan, 1987. **Agriculture in England: a survey of farming, 1870-1947**. Manchester.

Brown, Jonathan, 1991. **The Horse in Husbandry**. Ipswich.

Best, S.E.J., 1930. **East Yorkshire: a study in agricultural geography**.

Caird, J., 1852. **English Agriculture in 1850-51**.

Caune, Stephen, 1991. **Amongst Farm Horses: The Horselads of East Yorkshire**. Stroud.

Day, Herbert, 1985. **When Horses Were Supreme: The Age of the Working Horse**. Beverley.

Eddowes, J., 1854. **The Agricultural Labourer as He Really Is: Or, Village Morals in 1854**. Driffield.

Eddowes, J., 1854. **Martinmas Musings: Or Thoughts about the Hiring Day**. Driffield.

English, Barbara, 1990. **The Great Landowners of East Yorkshire**.

Everleigh, David, 1996. **The Victorian Farmer**. Princes Risborough.

Grigg, David, 1989. **English Agriculture. An Historical Perspective**. Oxford.

Gibbard, Stuart, 1997. **Change on the Land: A Hundred Years of Mechanised Farming**. Ipswich.

Haggard, H. Rider, 1902. **Rural England**.

Hall, Vance, 1987. **A History of the Yorkshire Agricultural Society 1837-1987**.

Harris, Alan, 1961. **The Rural Landscape of the East Riding of Yorkshire, 1700-1850**.

Harvey, N., 1984. **A History of Farm Buildings in England and Wales**. Newton Abbot.

Hayfield, C. and Brough, M., 1986-87. *Dewponds and pondmakers of the Yorkshire Wolds*. **Folk Life Journal 25**: 74-91.

Hayfield, C. and Wagner, P., 1995. *From dolines to dewponds: a study of water supplies on the Yorkshire Wolds*. **Landscape History 17**: 49-64.

Holderness, B.A. and Turner, M. (eds.), 1991. **Land, Labour and Agriculture, 1700-1920**.

Horn, P., 1976. **Labouring Life in the Victorian Countryside**. Dublin.

Horn, P., 1984. **The Changing Countryside in Victorian and Edwardian England and Wales**.

Howard, C., 1835. **A General View of the Agriculture of the East Riding of Yorkshire**.

Howkins, Alun, 1991. **Reshaping Rural England: a social history, 1850-1925**.

Jeffries, Richard, 1880 (1992 edition, with an introduction by Angela Richardson). **Hodge and his Masters**. Stroud.

Kirkwood, Norman, E., 1999. **To Farm Is To Live: An autobiographical account of farming in the East Riding of Yorkshire from the 1920s to the 1990s**. Driffield.

Kitchen, F. 1942. **Brother to the Ox: The Autobiography of a Farm Labourer**.

Leatham, Issac, 1794. **General View of the Agriculture of the East Riding of Yorkshire**.

Legard, F.D. (ed.), 1865. **More About Farm Lads**.

Legard, George, 1848. *Farming in the East Riding of Yorkshire*. **Journal of the Royal Agricultural Society of England 9**: 85-136.

Long, W. Harwood, 1969. **A survey of the agriculture of Yorkshire**.

Mills, D.R., 1980. **Lord and peasant in Nineteenth Century Britain**.

Milner, Eric, 1973. **Driffield Show Centenary 1973: The History of the Driffield Agricultural Society**. Driffield.

Mingay, G.E. (ed.), 1981. **The Victorian Countryside**. 2 volumes.

Mingay, G.E. (ed.), 1989. **The Unquiet Countryside**.

Morris, F.O., 1854. **The Present System of Hiring Farm Servants in the East Riding of Yorkshire with Suggestions for its Improvement**. Driffield.

Morris, M.C.F., 1928. **The British Workman Past and Present** [the life of William Blades, an East Riding farm worker during the late nineteenth and earlier twentieth centuries].

Neave, David, 1991. **Mutual Aid in the Victorian Countryside: Friendly Societies in the Rural East Riding 1830-1914**. Hull.

Newby, H., 1987. **Country Life: A Social History of Rural England**.

Overton, Mark, 1996. **Agricultural Revolution in England: The transformation of the agrarian economy, 1500-1850**. Cambridge.

Perry, P.J., 1974. **British Farming in the Great Depression 1870-1914: An Historical Geography**. Newton Abbot.

Pryor, Francis, 1998. **Farmers in Prehistoric Britain**. Stroud.

Reffold, Harry, 1984. **Pie for Breakfast: Reminiscences of a Farmhand**. Beverley.

Samuel, R. (ed.). **Village Life and Labour**.

Short, B. (ed.), 1992. **The English Rural Community: Image and Analysis**. Cambridge.

Simpson, Mary (ed. by F.D. Legard), 1861. **Ploughing and Sowing; Or, Annals of an Evening School in a Yorkshire Village, and the Work that Grew out of it**.

Simpson, Mary, 1865. *The Life and Training of a Farm Boy*. In F.D. Legard (ed.).

Simpson, Mary (ed. by F.D. Legard), 1876. **Gleanings: Being a Sequel to Ploughing and Sowing**.

Snell, K.D.M., 1985. **Annals of the Labouring Poor: Social Change and Agrarian England, 1600-1900**. Cambridge.

Somerville, A., 1852 (1989 edition). **The Whistler at the Plough**.

Street, A.G., 1934. **The Endless Furrow**.

Strickland, H.E., 1812. **General View of the Agriculture of the East Riding of Yorkshire**. York.

Thompson, Flora, 1945. **Lark Rise to Candleford**. Oxford.

Turner, Michael, 1980. **English Parliamentary Enclosure. Its Historical Geography And Economic History**. Folkestone.

Watts, Martin, 1999. **Working Oxen**. Princes Risborough.

Williams, Raymond, 1973. **The Country and the City**.

Woodward, Donald (ed.), 1984. **The Farming and Memorandum Books of Henry Best of Elmswell, 1642**.